Taming the Monkeys of the Mind

Or

Meditation for the Type A

By Emilio Robles

**Meditation Seminars are available;
contact us at:**

Our Web Page at

tamingthemonkeys.com
e-mail: dharma@caribe.net

Emilio Robles

2nd Edition 2007

ISBN: 0-9650060-2-6

Acknowledgements

To my wife Rita Maldonado
who thinks I'm so handsome
and whose superb knowledge
of the English language made
this book possible.

To my parents:

Araceli and Emilio
For their unconditional love and support.

Special thanks to:

Gadiel Hernández (Makeup Artist)
Ixiana Hernández (Photographer and Cover Designer)
David Wilmot (Cover Designer)

And to all my reviewers (a.k.a. helpful friends):
Lawrence Biscontini, Miguel de Jesús,
Francisco de Torres, Iván Figueroa,
Marla Mendelson, Ralph Nappi,
Osvaldo Robles, Paloma Blanca Robles,
Glen Siebert and David Storer

*"It is not so much our friends' help that help us
as the confident knowledge that they will help us"*

Epicurus – 3rd century BCE

"Do not believe in anything simply because you have heard it.

Do not believe in anything simply because it is spoken and rumored by many.

Do not believe in anything simply because it is found written in your religious books.

Do not believe in anything merely on the authority of your teachers and elders.

Do not believe in traditions because they have been handed down for many generations.

But after observation and analysis, when you find that anything agrees with reason and is conducive to the good and benefit of one and all, then accept it and live up to it."

The Buddha – 500 BC –

Preface

Some years ago I was sitting, quietly trying to calm my mind or meditate. When I finished, a friend came to me and told me: "You look so peaceful sitting there all by yourself; you resemble a big beautiful tree with a hundred branches spreading in all directions."

It was one of the best compliments I had ever received and I must say I was tempted, for the benefit of my egos, to leave it at that. However, it is always beneficial to speak the truth, therefore I replied to her: "Thank you for your kind words, but the truth is that, sitting on every branch of that tree there's a screeching monkey!"

Meditation has changed my life for the best. The monkeys haven't stop screeching yet... the only difference is that these days I don't pay them so much attention.

It is my very best wish that this book will do the same for you and that it will help you improve the quality of your life. I am sure that among the many alternatives that are suggested here you will find the ones that suit your personality and lifestyle. Enjoy!

Emilio Robles
El Yunque, Puerto Rico

Table of Contents

Appendix A - Meditation Tools and Techniques (Continued)

Introduction:

A Diploma From The School of Hard Knocks

"In the depth of winter, I finally learned that
there was within me an invincible summer."
-Albert Camus-

It is amazing how little I know about my own body and mind; I am afraid I know more about my car than my own anatomy and physiology. I check my car's fluid levels and pressures frequently and change the motor oil and filter every three thousand miles, I wash and wax it; I make sure the tires are balanced and change them before they lose their treads, I use good quality gas. I drive prudently, respecting all traffic signals, and I avoid the potholes and obstacles that could damage it. This behavior has paid off nicely: my car is in excellent condition and in all the years I have been driving, I have never had an accident.

On the other hand, for 42 years I paid no attention whatsoever to the needs of my body or the quality of the stuff I put into my mouth or my mind, whether I was well rested or not, and I could have cared less if my mind was in a state of constant turmoil. This behavior also paid off, but the currency was in pain and suffering.

I invite you to analyze the information presented here, and, as the Buddha said *"…if it agrees with reason and is conducive to the good and benefit of one and all, then accept it and live up to it ."* I am certain that by doing so you will avoid the emotional and physical potholes I *drove* my mind and body into and you will create a happier, healthier life. Here's my story:

Puerto Rico, where I was born, is a very beautiful island between the Caribbean Sea and the Atlantic Ocean. I like to think that the people born here are very warm and hospitable, maybe because not too long ago many of us were extremely poor. I have observed that frequently the people that have the least are the ones that give the most, because the joy of sharing makes us feel truly rich.

I am 64 years old. I was born in 1942 and I have lived all my life on the island, except for a two year stint (1965-67) as a Lieutenant and a Paratrooper in the US Army Signal Corps. My persona is an Electrical Engineer, Certified Data Processor, A+ and Network + Certified. I have worked in computers for over 30 years, from punched cards to Internet, you name it, and I've done it: build, sell, teach, network, program and maintain computers.

15

From 1973 to 1989 I owned a very successful business called Puerto Rico Computer, at the time I used to work very long hours. I also smoked a pack of cigarettes a day, drank over a dozen cups of Puerto Rican coffee, and was over 50 pounds overweight. I thought I was Superman. Finally I suffered the effect of the causes. In 1984, at age 42, during a fit of rage, I had a heart attack. To have a heart attack is a devastating experience and to have it at 42 years of age is doubly devastating since this is usually the age most of us are at the peak of our professional life.

After leaving the hospital I could barely walk fifty feet without feeling chest pains. As time passed, I became insufferable and unbearable. My partner of 18 years in the business left me and my wife of 23 years threatened to abandon me. I started to suffer anxiety attacks and I became suicidal. It was the worst of times... In my despair, I renounced everything I used to believe in. I had a Bible and one day I ripped it to shreds; I reasoned that this was just a collection of ancient little fables and if God really cared about us He (She?) would show His/Her face more often. Thus I challenged God: "You better show me your face if you love me, because I am going to kill myself!" I remember yelling.

I started making plans to commit suicide and was considering a gun as the means to terminate my life, but, since everything in this universe is interdependent, one day, as I was shooting pool at home with one of my son's friends, and without any apparent reason, he started to curse his father who had committed suicide some years before! I almost choked, to say the least! After this incident I carefully began to plan my death to make it look like an accident so that my family could not be stigmatized.

It took me about two weeks to come up with the solution to my dilemma... Every Saturday I used to go for a short swim at a nearby beach in San Juan called "El Escambrón". It is a small cove which at the time had a wood and metal bridge that spanned about 100 yards across the bay's inlet. I figured nobody would pay too much attention if I swam out into the Atlantic; eventually I would suffer hypothermia or a fish would eat me. They would find the car at the
16

parking lot and think I had accidentally drowned. It was perfect, or so I thought...

Soon enough the fateful Saturday arrived... I woke up relatively early, around 7:00 AM. I said goodbye to my wife in the most pleasant and natural way possible, as to not arouse suspiciousness, and drove toward the beach in my car a gray Buick Century. Traffic was almost non-existent, which is usual for an early Saturday, and very soon I reached "El Escambrón", parked my car at a nearby parking lot and walked toward the beach.

It was a glorious Caribbean day, the ocean and the sky vibrating with amazing hues of color, the strong scent of sargasso and iodine coming from the ocean, the sound of the waves against the breakers, gusts of wind buffeting my skin... and the sun... that sun of the Tropics, so vibrant and alive, flooding every living thing with energy. It was one of those days that make you feel you are going to live forever!

I began to walk over the bridge toward the other side where I thought would be the best spot to swim unnoticed into the ocean. I was on the middle of the bridge, when a young kid grabbed me by the left arm and stopped me... "Mister, mister, a man behind you jumped into the water!", he cried. Dazed I turned around and leaned over the railing to look under the bridge and, lo and behold!... there was an old man fully dressed crying for help and clinging to the bridge metal pylons for his dear life. Immediately the kid, with unbelievable speed, climbed the rail and dove from a height of 10 feet head-first into the green waters, then he swam close to the old man and encouraged him not to let go. "I am getting tired", the old man said. "Don't let go!" the kid replied, "I can't carry you, if you let go you `are going to get f-----d!", he finished saying. His words were tough but his manner wasn't, he was just a street kid expressing himself the best way he could.

Suddenly, I knew this was for me! I stepped over the rail on the planks protruding at the other side and jumped feet first into the sea, it was cold; I turned and faced the old man, from that moment on, everything seemed to happen in slow motion.

Ever since I first skin-dived under the bridge back in the late 50's I had always felt aversion for the underside of it. It was dark and gloomy, the rusty metal frame thickly encrusted with barnacles and seaweed. Waves rolled under it without breaking, like the back of a heaving leviathan, and as they rolled through, the beams and pylons hissed and sighed as if the bridge were alive... breathing. It was as beautiful on top of the bridge as it was menacing and ugly under it, as if nature somehow needed to balance itself.

As I swam toward the old man, I realized the bridge was too high to lift him from the water to the boardwalk; while pondering this situation somebody on the bridge threw us a life vest. The kid caught it and gave it to the old man who managed to put it on but could not tighten the straps because the vest was a child's size; I dove under and tightened a tiny, precarious knot with the safety straps. While under water I remember thinking: "Christ, if this knot becomes undone, it's two who are going to get f....d!" To this day this remains my most powerful prayer.

From the bridge they passed me a small board and I told the man to float on his back while grabbing one end of the board; I grabbed the other end and started to swim toward the shore using only my legs, in the breast-stroke style, praise the BSA, my Scout Master Mr. Baeza, and the Life Saving Merit Badge. We were halfway to the shore when somebody at the bridge shouted: "¡Tiburón!" (Shark!) I thought I saw a shadow passing under us. The old man started to panic. I'll be darned because; out of nowhere I heard myself asking him: "What is your name?" He looked at me as if I was insane, but somehow he calmed down and told me his name. The kid, God bless his soul, kept swimming around us and encouraging us to keep going...It must have been quite a sight: a street kid, and old man fully clothed, and myself, a failure of a man, all swimming together... I had to swim over 50 yards to reach the shore.

When I finally got the man safely on shore we both, soaking wet, sat on a nearby bench and I asked him... why he had jumped into the water? He told me a story that sounded remarkably familiar: "Three years ago I suffered a back injury that ruined my life; since then, my
18

life has been miserable and I have made the life of everyone around me miserable, too - I couldn't bear it anymore, so I decided to kill myself today!", he said. I immediately exclaimed: "But life is sacred!", then, as I realized what I was saying, I was overcome with uncontrollable shaking and my heart became arrhythmic. The crowd that had followed us from the bridge was now around us and started tending to the old man, hence I managed to slip unnoticed to my car, the car I never thought to see again, popped two Inderals into my mouth... and started to cry. What are the chances of being about to commit suicide and having to save another person's life... a zillion to one? Indeed, I had seen the face of God!

The Path to Recovery

"Life is either a daring adventure or nothing."
– Helen Keller -

Recovering from the heart attack has been a lifelong endeavor; after this remarkable incident I decided to put myself on the very top of the totem pole. I know it may sound selfish but it was not. I realized that, without me, there was not going to be a business or a family, so, for the past 20 years I practiced enhancing my life through exercise, relaxation and meditation. I totally changed my bearing in life...

I sold my business and moved from San Juan to the mountains, close to a rain forest reserve where I re-built an old cabin of a house. I have become certified in disciplines like Yoga, Pilates, Precision Cycling, Resist-A-Ball, Aqua Aerobics, and Group Exercise (AFAA). I became a C.H.E.K. Institute Exercise Coach and a certified Basic Anatomy and Physiology Instructor by the Department of Education. I teach this last subject at the Institute of Massage and Therapeutic Healing of Fajardo, Puerto Rico. I also teach Yoga and other holistic exercise disciplines at the Golden Door Spa at El Conquistador Hotel in Fajardo, Puerto Rico.

The results have been amazing: I am happy to say that I am in better shape now at age 64 than when I was 42. I have discovered throughout these years of practicing meditation, holistic exercises and other therapies that we can avoid future suffering. In other words, we can have a happier life if we take better care of our bodies. However, the reality is that most of us tend to live in a mental universe that takes the body for granted, thus, the mind abandons the body to fend for itself, in an autopilot limbo of sorts. This causes a chasm, or separation, between our mind and body. One of the main causes of this dichotomy is stress, the Archenemy of this age and time. Our minds get totally involved in a universe of hurries, worries, regrets, anger and attachment, and, in our blindness, these mental objects become very *physical* and take a constant and heavy toll on our bodies... which brings about a great deal of physical pain and suffering.

Our souls are incarnated in the bodies of primates, 98% of our DNA is identical to the chimpanzee's. For approximately 4 million years our bodies and minds adapted to survive in a hostile environment that seems indifferent to our needs. If we think in geological terms, it's only recently that we have managed to influence this environment in our favor through the use of our highly evolved minds. On the other hand, our bodies have not managed to evolve at the same rate as our minds. For our DNA to change one tenth of 1% it needs at least 100,000 years - not so our minds. Therefore, if we want to keep our bodies in optimal physical health, we must consider that the original design and purpose of our bodies was to survive, naked, outdoors in the African Savannah. Every time we use our body in a way that goes against the original design, a compromise should be reached if we want to keep ourselves healthy. For example: We go to bed past 10:00PM primates in the wild don't. Which are the consequences of this action? Have you ever seen a chimp in the jungle sit immovable, staring at a fixed object for eight hours, like we do when we work at the computer? Primates in the wild do not eat sugar by the ton like we do. Again this and other factors should be taken into account if we want to be healthy.

It seems to me that it is only logical to deduce that our bodies were designed to be used primarily to <u>move</u> in an <u>open</u> environment. I accordance to the previous hypothesis, what I have discovered through my studies and practices throughout these past years is that when we *live* in our minds, our bodies become rigid, and that **rigidity equals stress.** This rigidity is reflected in everything we physically do, in how we breathe, the way we move, we look (see), eat, talk, etc. Our neck and shoulders look as if we were carrying the weight of world on them. This, to me, is because we don't flow, we live totally disconnected from the needs of our bodies; we haven't taken the time to familiarize ourselves with its exquisite functioning; as I mentioned in the beginning, we are better acquainted with our cars than with our own flesh and blood.

I am a firm believer that through meditation (calming the mind), good posture, good breathing and movement (exercise), in other words, an all encompassing view of ourselves (holistic), we can certainly close the gap between our body and our mind and become healthier and happier human beings.

What is meditation?

"Be still and know that I am God."
46th Psalm, verse 10

Meditation is a state of serenity, balance, inner peace and well-being, regardless of the phenomena taking place outside or inside the practitioner. Meditation is keeping our cool no matter what!

One aspect of meditation is *mindfulness*. In my experience, this means that we pace, or synchronize, the mind to the body. It is a given fact that our minds are free from the time/space restrictions that apply to the body. The mind can fantasize, and/or go anywhere in the past or future, whenever it feels like it. Our body, however, cannot do this. By practicing mindfulness, we 'rev-down' the mind so that it restricts itself to the sequentiality of the present moment, where the body thrives. Then the mind becomes aware of the needs of its physical body in order to take better care of it, avoiding future pain and suffering.

Being stressful is the opposite of being mindful; it is an impossible, feeble attempt to synchronize our *slow* body to our *fast* mind. If tried long enough, it will bring dire consequences to the body. After the heart attack I started to suffer from random heart palpitations that my cardiologist called "premature beats". By observing myself I realized this happened when my mind was running amok and my heart tried unsuccessfully to catch up with it. This elevated my blood pressure and gave way to the "premature beats".

Magazines like Time (8/4/2003), Newsweek (9/27/2004), and National Geographic (March 2005) have dedicated editions to the mind and the benefits of meditation, just to name three of the myriad publications that have expounded on this subject.

In the early 1970's Dr. Herbert Benson, a graduate of Wesleyan University and the Harvard Medical School, through sound scientific methodology corroborated what the yogis have been telling us for centuries: meditation will make you a healthier person. In his article "Wallace and Benson, Scientific American 1972" he concluded that while meditating, the "relaxation response" will elicit (to mention just a few of the benefits) :

-    A greater number of alpha waves in the brain

- A reduction in the number of heartbeats
- A reduction in the consumption of oxygen
- A reduction in the generation of carbon dioxide
- A reduction in the levels of lactic acid
- A reduction in the blood pressure
- Lower metabolism

For further information on Dr. Benson's outstanding work please refer to his web page (The Relaxation Response Organization) at Appendix C.

If you allow it, meditation could be your antidote to stress. The benefits of meditation are many; this is common knowledge. We feel better, more relaxed and centered after a meditation session. Most of us have done some kind of meditation in our lives. Reading a good book, watching an inspiring film, playing with a child, jogging, even knitting... are all valid methods of taking ourselves to higher levels of consciousness. Meditation is not a struggle to control the mind. Part of our mind will always be assessing, labeling, judging and comparing, this is a basic strategy necessary for survival in the tri-dimensional universe we live in. Our meditation practice should first aim at lowering the *volume* of this internal dialogue; then, as our practice deepens, we will grow more accustomed to this inner serenity, until it remains with us all day, regardless of our surroundings.

Even though meditation has its origin in ancient spiritual practices, many of the techniques at our disposal are neutral; that is, we can reap their benefits regardless of our religious beliefs.

The Type A Personality

"Persona means "mask" in Greek.
You can always discard a mask."
-Emilio Robles-

In the 1950's Dr. Meyer Friedman, an American Cardiologist in San Francisco observed that the armrests and the edges of the chairs in his waiting room were worn out. From this he inferred that his patients were sitting, literally, at the edge of their seats while waiting to be called in. His clients were indeed very *impatient* patients.

Along with this characteristic, he also noticed that his patients tended to be workaholics; they were easily irritable, always busy, suffered hurry-sickness or time urgency, and could be easily provoked into a fit of anger. Dr. Friedman labeled this type of personality "Type A". In contrast with this personality type he found there was another behavior, which he labeled "Type B": the laid-back, easygoing type of person.

In 1984, after a series of studies, Dr. Friedman's hypothesis was recognized as a valid theory by the National Heart, Lung and Blood Institute. In Dr. Friedman's words: "Type A behavior is seldom recognized like it should: A major coronary risk factor". I have underlined the word "major" because when a doctor uses the word major to describe a risk factor what he really means in plain English is- this behavior can kill you! Take my word that it can, I've been there, done that. In 1984 I had a heart attack during a fit of rage.

Therefore, observe yourself. Are you like me, easily irritable and impatient most of the time? Do you feel the need to be in control more often than not? If the answer is yes, then you probably have a Type A personality.

In the next chapters we will see how we can mitigate the dire consequences this type of behavior can have in the quality of our health, relationships and overall enjoyment of life

A note about Dr. Friedman
Dr. Friedman was passionately in love with his work: cardiology and preventive medicine – among his many achievements we must include his work on the development of the cardiac catheter. As a young intern his colleagues nick-named him "Cannon Ball Friedman" because of his habit to rush to his patients' bedside at the hospital.

During his long and fructiferous life he suffered two heart attacks, and referred to himself as a "recovering type A." Dr. Friedman remained active to the very end of his life, spreading his compassionate teachings among his fellow humans, thus saving countless lives. He died on April 26, 2004 at the age of 90. Humanity has lost a champion of preventive medicine.

For a beautiful compendium of Dr. Friedman's life, please read the article written by Elaine Woo, Times Staff Writer at:

http://www.vegsource.com/articles/obit/friedman_latimes.htm

Should you be interested in his work I recommend the book: "*Type A Behavior and Your Heart*", which Dr. Friedman wrote with his colleague, Dr. Ray Rosenman.

A Few Words about Stress

"Future suffering can be avoided"
-Yoga Sutras - Patanjali - 200 BC-

In the 1950's Dr. Hans Selye gave the word stress its present definition: "A state where the body prepares to fight or flight in response to a real or imaginary situation (the stressor) that we perceive as threatening". Stress, therefore is a state that helps us survive the dangers on this planet.

The body reacts to perceived stress by secreting a series of hormones, among them adrenaline, which in turn will dilate the bronchioles, speed up the heartbeat, increase blood pressure, dilate the pupils, stop the secretion of saliva, slow digestion, slow bowel movements and delay the emptying of the colon and the bladder. This is known in scientific terms as becoming *sympathetic* or *catabolic*.

As you can see, the previous reactions are very physical, indeed! Under this *alarm response* the body expects you to either fight or flight by putting to good use the excess of adrenaline and other hormones in your bloodstream. After fighting or running away the body will understand that the event or stressor has been addressed and will then be able to go into a *relaxation response*. In scientific terms, the body then becomes *parasympathetic* or *anabolic*.

As for breathing, under the influence of certain stressors (i.e., an angry dog barking at us) we tend to inhale sharply and hold our breath, much like when cold water runs over our back. The opposite happens when we relax...when we feel relaxed, the breath is even, smooth and deep; our exhalations become long and effortless. Inhalation makes our heart beat faster and exhalation makes it beat slower. Doctors know this tendency as *respiratory sinus arrhythmia*; keep this fact in mind for future reference.

One of the major causes of our health problems is that most of the modern day stressors do not require a physical response hence we don't put to use the hormones that the body generates to cope with the stressful situation. Our sedentary lifestyles don't help much, either. Let's use a very common situation as an example: you don't like your work but you have financial obligations. You want to quit, but can't. This battle of the opposites in the <u>mind</u> will surely submit your <u>physical</u> body to continuous stress.

Making a habit of being continuously stressed causes the body to deteriorate physically and mentally; it is a known cause of heart disease, high blood pressure, stroke, ulcers, certain types of cancers and other illnesses. Medically speaking, what happens is that our body, out of habit, becomes addicted to the chemistry of stress hormones produced by our brain... with terrible consequences. On the other hand, being relaxed relieves physiological, chemical and hormonal loads on our body and brings about health, happiness, tolerance, serenity, peace and well-being for us and those around us.

I will now go back to Dr. Friedman's statement: "Type A behavior is seldom recognized like it should: A major coronary risk factor". This time I have underscored the words seldom recognized. Who seldom recognizes Type A behavior as a major coronary risk factor? I believe Doctor Friedman is referring to doctors and patients alike. But, why doctors? Aren't they health practitioners that should advice their patients to be aware of the harmful consequences of Type A behavior? I found the answer to this riddle talking to a close and dear friend, Dr. Ivan Figueroa, who is also a medical school professor (and my acupuncturist). He told me that nowadays, a medical student has so much knowledge to acquire in such a limited amount of time, that teaching prevention is not a priority at medical schools.

So, if not the doctor, who shall we turn to in our quest for a healthier life? The good news is: prevention is in our hands! We can incorporate changes in our lives to make our bodies and minds healthier. The Internet, with its great wealth of accumulated human knowledge is a fantastic tool we can use in making the right choices for a healthier lifestyle. In Appendix C you will find a few selected web sites that have helped me in this quest for wellness.

The fact that prevention is in our hands should empower us into fruitful action; however, most of us will make much needed radical changes in our lives only when a life-threatening sickness or a critical situation arises. Even then, some of us would rather die than change our lethal habits!

Why this suicidal behavior? I think neurology can give us the answer with its Law of Facilitation that states: "When an impulse passes once through a given set of neurons to the exclusion of others, it will tend to do so on a future occasion, and each time it traverses this path, the resistance will be smaller." Simply stated: is very difficult to break old habits because they are deeply *programmed* in our neural pathways. Changing habitual patterns will require quite some effort, surfing and gathering information over the Internet, no matter how magnificent the browser, won't be near enough! Yet I am positive that if you set your mind to it and apply this information, the results in your daily life will be outstanding!

Summarizing:
We are creatures of habit, good ones and bad ones; this booklet is about encouraging you to put into practice methods that can help you change for the best some of your less skillful habitual patterns in a way that will create a joyful, harmonious and healthy lifestyle This will take time, effort, perseverance, and commitment. Be patient and gentle with yourself, for this is a lifelong endeavor. Trust yourself and the universe will respond to your intent!

"Gnosis Se Authon" - Know Thyself

Inscription at Oracle of Delphi
Greece – 1400 BC

Before embarking on this quest for physical and mental health we should assess our capabilities and *know ourselves*. In other words, we should become aware of our strong points and our weaknesses. If this is not done we will be at risk of addressing symptoms and not causes, and it will be harder to succeed in our endeavors.

Your Nutrition
It is beyond the scope of this book to cover in detail such an important topic as nutrition, thus I am just going to give you some pointers and references to help you expand your knowledge on this crucial subject.

Your dwelling is as good as the building materials and the quality of the labor that was put into it; you can not build a quality home with cheap materials; the same applies to your body. The quality of your bones, ligaments, tendons, organs, tissue, mental processes, and body chemistry depends on the quality of the food you eat. It is in your best interest that you select and ingest quality nutrients. By the same token in order to sit calmly and meditate your body has to be well nourished.

Today America is suffering an epidemic of obesity and malnutrition. Sodas, caffeine, alcohol, smoking, white sugar, artificial sweeteners, white flour, excess salt, artificial colors and flavors, and fast foods don't provide the necessary nutrients for health. You are doing a disservice to yourself and your family when you consume these products because they make you unhealthy and prone to sickness; you won't be able to concentrate and will be more likely to suffer from depression, irritability, lack of energy, and all kinds of mood swings. This was fully illustrated on the film "Super Size Me" by Morgan Spurlock. However, if you change your diet to include whole, organic foods and drink 8 glasses of pure (not chlorinated) water a day I guarantee that you will feel vibrant, alive, healthier and happier!

I have used with success the book *How to Eat, Move and Be Healthy!* by Paul Chek, which includes questionnaires that address nutrition and lifestyle issues and helped me determine my metabolic type. By

41

selecting a diet adequate for my genetic profile, I now feel better nourished and more satisfied.

I also recommend two books by Carol Simontacchi: *The Crazy Makers* and *Natural Alternatives to Vioxx, Celebrex & Other Anti-Inflammatory Prescription Drugs*. These books provide valuable information in the fields of nutrition and holistic remedies. In *The Crazy Makers*, Ms. Simontacchi talks about the effects the American diet is having on us, especially on our youth. In *Natural Alternatives to Vioxx, Celebrex & Other Anti-Inflammatory Prescription Drugs* she teaches us how to avoid and prevent chronic inflammations using natural alternatives, a must read for all of us daily pain sufferers that want to enjoy a 'natural' painless day.

The Quality of Your Sleep
The quality of your health is also directly linked to the quality of your sleep. To properly repair your mind and body you need eight hours of sleep *or more* every night. To improve the quality of your sleep remove the TV from your bedroom and switch to reading at least one hour before falling asleep to give your body a chance to wind down and prepare for the night's rest. Your room should be totally dark, no lights should shine into your room from the street or from adjacent rooms, and it should be as sound-proof as possible. Make a point of going to bed by 10:00 PM, your body will love it! Many people have been cured of very 'serious illnesses' by merely drinking 8 glasses of water a day and sleeping 8 hours a night!

Assessing Our Mind
We should prepare for meditation like we would for physical exercise; both are challenging tasks, the only difference is that in meditation we are training our mind instead of our body. It is my experience that the causes of most of our problems are mental; everything starts in the mind and then 'spreads' to the body. Be it happiness or misery, the process is the same. Just like we assess our physical condition before starting an exercising program we should start a meditation program by assessing first our **social environment**, our **family environment**, our **working environment** and the effects these have in our well-being.

42

Issues of Forgiveness – Keep in mind that when you evaluate your social, family and working environment you will find a common thread running through them: grudges, bad memories and regrets. Stay aware, identify them, because if you ignore them they will drain you and take you to an early grave. Make a list, work them out of your system, consult them with your spiritual counselor, get professional help if necessary...otherwise, holding on to these unresolved issues will tear your body and your soul to pieces. Let go and forgive, forgive, forgive seven times seventy. It is in your own best interest to release this resentment and put to good use this bottled up energy! You'll be surprised by how much better you will feel when forgiveness opens your heart.

There is an excellent book: *The Wisdom of Forgiveness* by the Dalai Lama and Victor Chan that will definitely help you cope with this extremely important subject better than I possibly could.   When assessing your social, family and working environment, remember to keep yourself on your toes in order to detect deeply ingrained patterns of resentment in your psyche.

The Social Environment
The social environment we live in is not the most conducive to reflection.   We are constantly bombarded by the media with outrageous news, by Hollywood's glorification of violence, and by television's omni-present ads enticing us to buy this or that.   The Internet and its tsunami of e-mails plus our myriad responsibilities all come together to snatch from us our must precious asset: *time*.   Be aware of this fact when you turn on the TV, the radio or the computer, whenever you go to the movies or a mall!

Time is the only asset that you will never have enough of. Therefore, the key to create happiness for ourselves and others is to set aside time for exercise and meditation on a <u>daily basis</u>. We could follow the same recommendations for meditation as the experts recommend for exercise: **accumulate 30 minutes** every day of any type of meditation technique you find suitable.   In Appendix A, titled Meditation Tools and Techniques, I offer many options that in my case have proven to be very effective; I suggest you analyze them and determine which of them suit your lifestyle and personality best.

The Family Environment – Past and Present

A lot of the mental patterns that we presently exhibit were learned within our family environment. The family environment plays the most important role in the development of our personalities. We should make our very best effort to maintain an environment of peace and harmony in our home; we should also assess the family environment we grew up in and/or that we are living in right know. *Do not hesitate to seek professional help if necessary.*

I am not a trained mental health professional but I know this from personal experience: our children don't really need the latest, most expensive technological gizmo on the market... what they really need is that we love and cherish them, that we spend quality time with them, gaining their willing trust and confidence. If we love them well now, they will be able to draw from this 'well' of love and wisdom in their adulthood, and their lives will have an increased potential for balance and harmony.

Do you think, like I used to, that you don't have time for your children because of your work? Then delegate some of your work's responsibilities and make time for it! If you don't spend quality time with your children the drug dealer will! Drug dealers have plenty of time to spend with your children, listen to them and empathize with them, in case you don't. Keep in mind that frequently drug dealers are their peers! You could set a basketball court or a Ping-Pong table at home, join the Boy/Girl Scouts – it will do both your child and yourself a lot of good. If you can afford it, get a boat, trailer home, or both...see the country! I encourage you to hike, camp, and picnic with your family every weekend from here to kingdom come.

To re-kindle the relationship with your spouse, why not go on a vacation alone, without the children... Even a weekend will do! Raising children is a big challenge that can put a huge strain in the marriage; couples need to be close to succeeding in raising their children. Devote your weekends to your family, not your work! This is the best advice I can possibly give you. You'll love it!

If you are a single parent, it is twice as important that you take good care of yourself. Whenever possible, rest. Avoid masking your fatigue with stimulants (like soda or coffee), but make sure you accumulate 30 minutes of both meditation and exercise daily, nourish yourself and your loved ones with quality nutrients and sleep well; then you will have the energy and vitality to make this double challenge a doubly satisfying task! Now, you might say: *But I don't have time for myself!* I, too, used to say that before I had the heart attack; and, even though I worked 16 hours a day, guess what?...I still found time to waste on TV and movies! If I had used that time to exercise, to sleep, to rest and to meditate I probably would not be writing this book today!

The Environment at Work

The Japanese concede that high levels of stress in the work-place can kill you; they name this effect *karoshi*. Consider this: usually you spend more time at work than with your family. Be aware that the eight hours you spend at home sleeping, in order for your body and mind to be healthy, really don't count as time with the family.

The National Institute for Occupational Safety and Health (NIOSH) is the Federal Agency responsible for conducting research and making recommendations for the prevention of work-related illness and injury. On their web page (Appendix C), they have very interesting and comprehensive information on work related stress.

NIOSH defines job stress as the harmful physical and emotional response that occurs when the requirements of the job do not match the capabilities, resources, or needs of the worker and can lead to poor health and even injury. Following are some of the results from two out of the many surveys you will find on their web page:

-National Life Survey - 40% of the workers interviewed
  referred to their jobs as "very or extremely stressful".

-A survey conducted by St. Paul Fire and Marine Insurance Company indicated that problems at work are more strongly associated with health complaints than are any other life stressors, more so than even financial problems or family problems.

If you are a manager: I worked as an independent software programmer for 16 years during which I developed hundreds of pieces of software for many, many companies. I went into the inner sanctum of small, middle, and Fortune 500 companies. This gave me the unique opportunity to observe closely different working environments and management styles, from bosses that ran their show like despots, all the way to elegant, savvy managers that treated people at all levels with respect and trust, and were both firm and fair in their managerial decisions.

I also observed that employees imitate their boss' style. If the boss growls in the morning instead of sharing a good morning and a genuine smile with the employees, sooner or later everybody at the office will be growling. Furthermore, everybody will take this growling over to their homes! If you are a manager you have *the unique opportunity* of improving the quality of your work environment and decreasing the levels of stress for every one by acting out of goodwill. By doing this, you will exert a positive influence on countless souls; it won't only be your employees but also their families and friends...probably even their pets! Good manners, fairness, openness, and kindness are contagious. As the old Spanish saying goes: "Lo cortés no quita lo valiente" (Being courteous doesn't make you less brave!).

Mobbing: There is also a more sinister, subtle stressor at work we haven't become fully conscious of yet and that is lethal: the act of **mobbing,** or *horizontal violence,* also known as *psychological terror* in the work environment. Dr. Heinz Leymann, a Swedish psychologist and medical scientist, pioneered the research about this workplace issue in the early 80's. Mobbing occurs when a group of co-workers consciously or unconsciously gang-up to force someone out via intimidation, humiliation, sarcasm, harassment, rumor, innuendo, etc. Therefore, in this quest for self-knowledge, ask yourself four important questions about your work:

First: Do I like my work? Or, better yet… do I love it? After all, you are spending more time at work than with your dear ones.

Second: Do I treat others (up and down the managerial ladder) courteously and fairly?

Third: Do my supervisors **and** my peers at work treat me fairly? For example: When I put in extra effort, is it appreciated?

Fourth: Is there mobbing at work? – Do I participate in it, or am I its victim?

Depending on the answers, you might discover that you are either in a good working environment, or that maybe it is time for a change, like finding a new job or starting your own business. Remember: your mental sanity is at stake, if you want to live a less stressful life don't ignore the effects your working environment has on you.

Exercising Our Body

An article in the July/August 2004 edition of the American Council on Exercise Fitness Matters Magazine states: "no matter your age, starting an exercise program not only will boost your physical fitness, it may also improve your thinking ability as well." The quality of our physical health greatly influences the quality of our meditation; as the Immortal Bard once said: "There was never yet philosopher that could endure the tooth-ache patiently." It is necessary, then, that our body be in good shape for our meditation to prosper. Following this line of thought, it is of utmost importance that we examine our actual physical condition before embarking in an exercise program. The family doctor can order a battery of tests to establish our blood pressure, cholesterol/triglycerides levels, etc. This will set a baseline to start from and refer back to. It will also minimize the risk of injuries and setbacks.

Along the same line of thought, the services of a qualified personal trainer are most valuable to determine our current levels of cardiovascular fitness, body composition, muscular strength and endurance, flexibility, as well as musculo-skeletal and postural imbalances. Some personal trainers are qualified to perform a *physiological load assessment* of their clients. This is a holistic type of evaluation that goes further than the regular evaluations performed in the gym setting. It takes into account the client's lifestyle and the overloads to their musculo-skeletal, hormonal and emotional systems. A holistic evaluation will consider the *physiological load* produced by factors such as: daily water intake, sleep quality, and eating in accordance with our metabolic type. It will take into account our postural imbalances, or even whether our job demands too much from one side of our brain. These important factors are then used to fine-tune exercise routines whereas they match *both* our physical and mental fitness levels.

According to common sense, start a fitness program gradually, taking into account your actual physical condition. Then build up slowly but consistently. In this manner, the risk of injury is minimized and the enjoyment of the fitness program is maximized. The National Institute of Health recommends that children and adults alike should set a goal of accumulating at least 30 minutes of moderate-intensity physical activity on most, and preferably, all days of the week. This goal will probably be increased in the near future.

On page 95 you will find a check list of the more important goals mentioned in this book, in order to facilitate the planning of your journey to a healthier life!

Breathing: The Key to Vanquish Stress.

"The best things in life are free"
-Anonymous-

The Mechanics of Breathing - To be able to meditate properly you need to breathe properly, which makes the following information crucial if you want to succeed in the art of meditation.

One might think that there is nothing new to breathing; after all, we've been doing it since we were born! We might also think that breathing is automatic and we shouldn't have to be concerned about it. These assumptions are only partially right, because breathing is an intriguing function of our bodies: it can be controlled both voluntarily and/or involuntarily. The involuntary control is taken care of in our bodies by the autonomous nervous system. The involuntary control overrides our voluntary control, which explains why we can't kill ourselves just by holding our breath. On the other hand and within certain limits, we can willfully affect our breathing patterns.

Most of us have bad breathing habits which have a direct effect in the way we move, think, and feel. Breathing patterns are directly linked to our emotional states. For thousands of years the yogis have been studying breathing patterns and their effect in our minds and bodies; they call this art-science Pranayamas. B.K.S. Iyengar, a great master of yogis (Yogacharia) has written extensively about breathing patterns in his book 'Light on Pranayamas'. Before we go any further, let's look at some of the anatomical and physiological features in our body that are involved in breathing. Please refer to Figure 1 on the next page.

This figure represents a bottle with its bottom cut off and replaced with a flexible membrane that we can pull down like in fig. 1-B. At the mouth of the bottle we have fitted an inverted **Y** tube and at the end of each branch we have placed a balloon. When the bottom membrane is at rest (Figure 1-A) the balloons are collapsed. When we pull down on the membrane (Figure 1-B), a partial vacuum is created inside the bottle and the balloons expand in response, drawing air from the outside of the bottle. As a result, the balloons expand and fill with air.

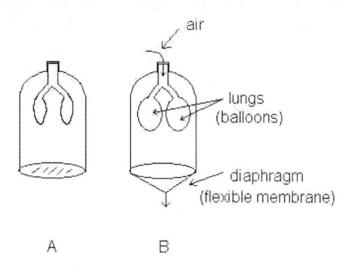

Figure 1

The bottle represents our ribcage or thoracic cavity, the membrane is the diaphragm (the muscle that seals the bottom of our ribcage), the inverted **Y** represents the bronchi, and the balloons are the lungs. The mouth of the bottle stands for our nose/mouth apertures where the air enters and exits. This is an overly simplistic model of our respiratory system, but it serves the purpose of helping describe the following: as the diaphragm contracts, it moves down and the lungs fill with air; this action is called inspiration or inhalation. When the diaphragm relaxes, the lungs collapse and the air is expelled through our mouth and/or nose, and this is called expiration or exhalation.

To a certain extent (remember, we can't commit suicide by holding our breath) we have volitional control of the muscle we call diaphragm. We can hold it taut at the end of our inspiration or we can keep it relaxed at the end of the exhalation, even if it is for a limited amount of time. We can willfully increase or decrease the speed of the respiratory cycle. By taking short, shallow breaths we can make it very fast, or we can make it very slow by taking long inhalations and exhalations. We can also choose to inhale through our mouth or through our nose; the same possibility exists for our exhalation. For example, by exhaling through our pursed lips we can make our exhalations longer than our inhalations. If we wish we can retain the breath for a short time after exhalation, inhalation, or both. Furthermore, using our fingers to push gently at the side of our nostrils we can control through which nostril (left or right) the air will flow when inhaling or exhaling. We can also partially close our throat, or more specifically, the glottis, and restrict the passage of air, sounding somewhat like Darth Vader, the villain from the Star War Series!

We can do all the previous breathing maneuvers while holding a different posture, like standing on our feet, on our head, sitting, lying on our back or on our belly, etc. As you can see, there are many ways to influence our breathing and our physiological states by practicing control of our respiratory functions, but it is far beyond the scope of this book to cover them all here. I just wanted to make you aware of the baffling amount of possibilities available in the practice of breathing, something that most of us take for granted. Some yogis say that one life-time is not enough to explore them all.

Let's go back to our bottle. As I mentioned, this is a simplified model of our respiratory system, since the diaphragm is not the only muscle involved in breathing. If you place your hands on your rib cage, you will feel it expand to the front, sides, and back from the bottom to the top when inhaling and then collapse when exhaling...*our bottle is also flexible!* This movement of the ribcage is due in part to the action of the inter-costal muscles, the muscles between our ribs.
Our abdominal musculature also plays an important role in breathing. It distends during the inhalation and contracts (bringing the belly button in) during the exhalation, thus assisting the diaphragm in forcing the air out of the lungs. Another set of muscles in the neck usually assists at the end of the inhalation cycle by pulling up the ribcage.

To determine your type of breathing let's do an experiment: Sitting tall, begin by releasing your belt a couple notches, hence nothing binds your waist. If loosening your belt is not enough, or if you are wearing tight pants, you might just want to open the top button and lower your pants' zipper. Place your left hand over your belly button and your right hand over your sternum, the breast plate that protects your heart. Take a deep breath and observe the movement of your hands, if any.

This is what you should feel: upon inhalation your belly button should move out followed by the expansion of your chest or rib cage. The reverse should occur during the exhalation cycle: your rib cage should contract, or sort of collapse, followed by the contraction of your abdomen. This is usually called abdominal breathing and is normally the way babies breathe, it is effortless and very relaxing.

A common dysfunctional breathing pattern consists of breathing by moving the chest with almost no abdominal movement. This is called constricted chest breathing, or shallow breathing, and it generates considerable upper body tension. H. David Coulter, Ph.D., in his book *Anatomy of Hatha Yoga*, and Erik Peper, Ph.D. and Vicci Tibbetts, M.A., of the Institute for Holistic Healing Studies in San Francisco State University, in their excellent paper *Effortless Diaphragmatic Breathing*, coincide in pointing out that chest breathing can eventually lead us to physical and mental problems such as: elevated heart rate and blood pressure, poor digestion and elimination, habitual stressful behavior, etc.

Furthermore, some of us tend to breathe in a manner that totally opposes abdominal breathing. That is, the abdomen moves *in* rather than out when inhaling and moves *out* rather than in when exhaling. This is known as paradoxical breathing, a pattern of the worst kind because it immediately shoots a jolt of adrenaline through the body and strains the heart. Chest breathing and paradoxical breathing keep the sympathetic nervous system in a state of constant arousal, adversely affecting digestion, circulation, endocrine, immune and sexual function. If you breathe like this you should correct it *pronto*!

There are other dysfunctional breathing patterns like intermittent inhalations or exhalations, just to mention a few. In my case, I have to make a special effort while writing these pages in my computer to avoid restricting my breathing to the upper chest, which results in over-use of the neck muscles. This is a very tense and tiring type of breathing; I am also convinced it is a component of my tendency to experience high blood pressure. I look at it as one of those bad habits I mentioned at the beginning of the book. As a child, I probably tensed up when learning new things, whether they were threatening or not, and this alarm response became deeply ingrained in my psyche.

Even though these faulty breathing patterns could predispose our body to sickness; we can **learn** new healthy habits! The purpose of this book is to empower ourselves out of these conundrums, be they postural, respiratory and/or mental, thus improving by a quantum leap the quality of our general well-being!

Effortless Diaphragmatic Breathing with Long Exhalations

Of all the available breathing patterns there is one I would like to share with you, my dear reader, because of its importance for our well-being. This breathing pattern greatly improved the quality of my life, and of all the many breathing patterns yoga has to offer, it captured my interest the minute I learned about it. Capturing my interest quickly was the key, for, in case you haven't guessed, like Dr. Friedman, I am a recuperating type A.

But first, allow me to digress a bit... Yoga is a four-in-one discipline that encompasses love (towards one-self and others), exercise, breathing and meditation. The discipline of Yoga is at least 7,000 years old, and it is speculated that it could be older, possibly 10,000 years old. This is a remarkable lifespan for any human endeavor. I think yoga has survived for such a long time because the ancient sages who developed it arrived at outstanding conclusions through experience gleaned from keenly observing human behavior. Nowadays modern science confirms that the teachings of these ancient sages are sound and valid ways to improve our health.

The Yogis believe that we are born with a given amount of heart beats; we could call it a genetic predisposition that determines our lifespan. Imagine that the second we are born a count-down starts, and every time our heart beats the counter subtracts one from the

55

original amount until eventually, at the end of many, many years (hopefully as many as we need) it reaches zero, and then we die ☹.

I'm not suggesting we take this teaching literally, but I would like you to consider it as a model that could help us improve our health. From the yogis' perspective, then, it makes sense to save our heart beats, whenever possible we should make our heart beat slower, consequently we will live longer. Think of it this way: every time we stress-out our whole body becomes sympathetic and we waste energy and precious heart beats. It would make perfect sense, in order to live longer, to make a habit of staying as relaxed as possible, enhancing our parasympathetic threshold. Anger makes our heart beat faster, and who could doubt that this emotion might take years from our life?

Let's go back to the effortless diaphragmatic breathing with long exhalations. Since no breathing technique will work properly unless our posture is good; like my mother used to say: "Don't slouch!" First make sure you are wearing loose clothing, then sit comfortably on a chair in a quiet corner, feet flat on the floor, hands resting on your thighs. Avoid crossing your legs. Extend your spine fully but maintain its natural curves, don't collapse or flex forward, instead, gently lift the chest up. Your chin should be parallel to the ground, ears aligned over the shoulders and shoulders over the hip joint.

The object of this exercise is to elicit the relaxation response. Inhale <u>deeply</u> through your nose (distending the abdomen) and at the same time mentally count the length of the inhalation. Now, gently purse your lips and exhale slowly through the mouth, counting the duration of your exhalation. You will observe that naturally and effortlessly the exhalation lasts longer than the inhalation.

With this type of breathing you will use to your advantage the "respiratory sinus arrhythmia", or the fact that your heart rate increases during inhalation and decreases during exhalation. Breathing in this manner for <u>a couple of minutes</u> will make you more *anabolic* or *relaxed*. Since I have the habit of spending a lot of time worrying and hurrying, in order to help me develop this breathing pattern I set my wrist watch to beep every hour on the hour; when it does, I take a couple of deep breaths through the nose with exhalations through the mouth. If I am feeling particularly stressed-out, I practice it more often.

Another advantage this type of breathing offers is that it is very discrete, no one will notice that you are breathing this way; therefore you can practice it wherever and whenever you feel like it! Take special note to relax your neck and shoulder muscles when learning deep breathing in this way initial acquisition of the skill is free of alarm responses. Easy-does-it approach will work best when learning; avoid excessive striving, as Dr. Peper's paper well advices.

Important Notice – If you have *low blood pressure* be careful when practicing deep breathing with long exhalations, because there is a possibility that you could faint!

Summary: Undoubtedly, relaxation soothes our mind, calms our emotions, and centers our being; and it is an important component of the regenerative and healing process of our mind and body that helps us lead a healthy and harmonious life. In the process of reaching a relaxation state, the healing power of breathing must not be underestimated. Deep breathing is a deceivingly simple technique that is most effective. I am aware that many people think that if something's not shaped like a pill it won't be able to heal us... let us gently start changing this view.

About Meditation Tools and Techniques

"...the kingdom of heaven is within"
-Matthew (4.17)-

After studying and practicing different meditative techniques for many years I have come to believe that once you reach the final state of meditation, or *enlightenment* (also known as *Samadhi* or *Absolute Bliss*), you will become one with God, Knowledge and/or Transcendental Wisdom; you will understand the true nature of things and your quest will be over for you will have reached the ultimate goal… Samadhi or Unconditional Love.

I would like to clarify at this moment that the closest I have come to being *enlightened* is when I turn on a light switch! Nevertheless, I have had the opportunity to be in close company of those who are, or who have almost achieved this goal. They have become my inspiration, because they are the living proof that my goal is attainable. When you are in the presence of one of these beautiful beings you get a feeling of total acceptance and lack of judgment. You are '*cool*' just the way you are. Furthermore, if you have the privilege to hug one of them, it feels as if you were embracing the air, or something very light. The best way I can describe it is by saying that they just don't project the heaviness of the human ego. But, what is meditation for us, mere mortals? We can begin by *bringing the mind to the present moment*. This is a feat that should not be underestimated; its difficulty is best summed up in this ancient saying…"The untrained mind is like a drunken elephant, who can tell it where to go and what to do?"

"Know thyself". Through observation of my thought patterns I have noticed that when I am not challenged by my job, studies, prayers or any other particular action that demands my full attention, my mind would generally wander into one of the following three directions:

1. The past – to relive memories, regret what I did, should have done, and/or didn't do.

2. The future – to generate all kinds of mental constructs, or to worry and depress *ad nauseam* about a thousand terrifying projections…

3. The present – to label, compare and/or judge.

61

I conclude that, while it is quite OK to ponder the experiences of the past and use those to plan for the future, one should not become obsessed about them, like I have done more times than I wish to remember. Applying too much time and energy to time frames that are gone or yet to be generates huge amounts of <u>mental</u> stress which, as we know, also affects our physical body. Mental stress is the worst kind, because we cannot fight or flee to relieve it. Also, it makes little sense to spend our only available time, the present, engaged in endless judgments and comparisons. At this junction, meditation and/or relaxation techniques become valuable antidotes to stress, and we can gently and compassionately use them to substitute unskillful mental patterns for healthier ones.

Again, analyzing past experiences and spending time labeling reality in order to plan ahead are skills necessary to succeed in life. It's the *relentless, obsessive quality of our thinking processes* that blocks us from generating wellness, equanimity and joy. As I mentioned, there is only **one** meditative state: "The state of serenity, inner peace, of well-being, regardless of the phenomena taking place outside or inside the practitioner." These are good news! There is just one goal to achieve: and it feels<u> **really good,**</u> physically, mentally and spiritually!

The Space - Last, but not least, I recommend that you select an area in your home, it doesn't need to be too big, and a corner in a room will do, and determine that this is going to be your meditation space. You can decorate this space any way you see fit; everything works well as long as you feel comfortable with it. Your meditation space can be as Baroque or as Spartan as you wish. The idea is that the *energy* of this space should beckon you to meditate, just like your TV beckons you to watch it, or the fridge beckons you to eat!

In my space I sometimes have flowers, a picture of the goals (material or spiritual) I want to achieve, photographs of my loved ones and spiritual teachers, an incense burner and a chair... at my age it is easier to sit on a chair than to sit on my knees or the floor. It may also help to wear special garments (cap, t-shirt, etc.) when you are going to meditate, as if to tell the mind: "Hey! We are going to meditate... start chilling!"

Appendix A

Meditation Tools and Techniques
(In alphabetical order)

-George Bernard Shaw-

For many years I have practiced the techniques that I mention here. Each of them has been of incalculable value to me in solving the puzzle of my Type A behavior and quieting down the monkeys of my mind. Even though some might only suit my style, I encourage you to use them or any other technique you may discover, as long as you feel they bring harmony, peace and balance to your inner self. When it applies, I have also made every possible effort to give credit to those compassionate beings that worked so hard in making these wonderful techniques possible and available.

A candle to remember

In this cacophonous world it is easy to forget... forget special events, or forget special occasions. On special days (somebody's birthday or for someone in need) I light a fragrant candle in my meditation space to help me remember to send good wishes and prayers throughout the day to this person and to any or all in need.

Aloneness

Sometimes I enjoy being alone, away from everyone, even from my loved ones. I sit under a tree or on the beach all by myself to ponder the mysteries of this universe; here we are, floating on a grain of sand traveling through space in a galaxy among an infinite number of galaxies...

Aromatherapy

Fragrant candles, incense, scented eye pillows, essential oil on your temples before going to bed, an aromatic bubble bath, the smell of good hot soup, or of freshly baked cinnamon bread...hmm...these are just a few examples of how good we feel when we smell certain fragrances. I invite you to use them while meditating.

Edward Bach (1886-1936), a British Surgeon who became dissatisfied with conventional medicine, launched himself on a one-man crusade in the 1930's to find alternate, more compassionate ways to ease human suffering. He concentrated his endeavors in studying the effects flowers' fragrances had in alleviating emotional and mental dysfunctions. When I researched his work on the Internet I got 57,943 hits! You might be interested in taking a closer look at his amazing discoveries. From traditional aromatherapy, here are just a few of the fragrances we can use to harmonize our moods and emotions:

- o   Rose – from anger to peace
- o   Patchouli – from anxiety to acceptance
- o   Orange – from depression to joy
- o   Cedar Wood – from fear to courage
- o   Rose, Sandalwood – from grief to happiness
- o   Lavender – from irritability to openness
- o   Ylang Ylang – from stress to trust

You may wish to enjoy any of these essential oils in scented candle form, burn them in a diffuser, or add drops of them to a sleeping eye mask. One of the greatest advantages of aromatherapy is that you do not have to do anything but breathe it! Once the essential oils are inhaled, your body will respond by easing into a relaxation response.

Breathing (see page 51)
"If you control your breathing you will control your emotions", states one of the sutras, or aphorisms by the ancient yogis. This is easier said than done. Trying to "hold our horses" when we get upset is almost impossible for our untrained minds. Most of us fall victim to the monkeys of our emotions.

Remember that one of the ways we jump start our sympathetic system (fight or flight response) is by inhaling sharply and holding our breath for a short time. To induce a relaxation response (parasympathetic system) we should breathe slowly and deeply, lengthening our exhalations. Physiologically speaking, it makes a lot of sense to breathe in the manner that suits the occasion...

Try this the next time you feel anxious, fearful, upset or angry: inhale quietly and deeply through the nose, and then exhale through the mouth, making the exhalation as long as possible. Invariably you will relax. The challenge here consists of trying to break our habitual pattern. It requires constant practice, like learning to ride a bike; but once you learn the skill you will never forget it!

Another powerful breathing technique that helps induce relaxation and lowers your brain's activity is known as *alternate nostril breathing*. It is very simple, yet very effective: you inhale and exhale through the nose only, and use the thumb and ring finger of the right hand to control the flow of air through your right and left nostrils respectively. The index and middle fingers are bent toward the palm of the hand or rest on the forehead to keep them out of the way. Begin by taking a deep, slow inhalation through both nostrils and then gently press your right nostril closed using the thumb of your right hand. Exhale through your left nostril, which is open. Keeping the right nostril closed inhale through the left nostril, then use your ring finger to gently close your left nostril, remove your thumb from your right nostril and exhale and inhale through it. Again press the right nostril with your thumb and repeat the exhalation/inhalation cycle on the other nostril... and so on.

Do this type of breathing for at least five minutes. It will relax and soothe your mind, balancing both hemispheres of the brain. Even though these breathing exercises are simple, keep in mind that the idea is to relax, so, do not strain, and avoid if having congested nasal passageways. Again, for more information on this science-art, refer to "Light on Pranayamas" by B.K.S. Iyengar, or join a yoga class that includes Pranayamas.

Children

Since I have five grandchildren, I have had ample opportunity to discover how relaxed I feel when playing with them! Playing with children constitutes active meditation, which is great for Type A's who multi-task their way to relaxation: staying present and spending quality time with our children can happen simultaneously!

What kind of meditation technique can we learn from children? When playing, children live intensely in the here and now; they don't waste much time being worrywarts. They teach us trust and enthusiasm, and their innocence and energy is contagious. By the way, the best present you can give a child is not a toy, but time spent in undivided love and attention...try storytelling, nature walks, or making dolls!

Concentration Drills

Here are four drills that will help increase your concentration power. To prepare, just sit quietly with good posture and take a couple of deep breaths with long exhalations (see page 55), then:

- Bring your awareness to the *tip of the nose* and feel the temperature of the air as it enters and exits your body; cool upon entering and warm on the way out. When your mind strays, gently bring it back to the tip of the nose. Start with 5 minutes, aim for 20 minutes.

- Slowly count down <u>your exhalations</u> from 10 to 0; **if your mind wanders off, begin again at 10**. Try to make the number last the length of your exhalation, for example: Teeeeeeeennnnnnn or Sixxxxxxxxxxxxx. Keep increasing the starting number until you can count down from 100 to 0 without your mind getting distracted.

- Light a candle or place a flower in front of you and look at it without blinking. When you feel like you can't keep your eyes open any longer, close your eyes and cup them with the palms of you hands, being careful not to apply pressure on the eyeballs.

  With eyes closed, bring to your mental screen all the details of the object of your concentration. Repeat for 5-15 minutes.

- After you have mastered the previous drill try the following variation: upon closing your eyes imagine that you are looking at yourself from the candle or flower's viewpoint. See how many details you can remember about yourself, you will be amazed!

Note: When your mind wanders off in any of the previous exercises, bring it back to the task at hand gently, as you would do with a child. It'll take some time to succeed in your practice, maybe a couple of weeks if you are willing to practice every day...please be patient with yourself.

Dancing

Hey, who said meditation couldn't be fun? Dancing, besides being great for body and soul, provides a combination of music and movement that can induce a meditative trance, as exemplified by the Sufi Masters of Islam. All you have to do is *be mindfully there*!

Osho, a great meditation teacher of the late part of the 20th century, taught meditation techniques using music and dancing. See Appendix D for his web address.

Doing Nothing, Loafing or Mesmerizing Yourself

One of the characteristics of the Type A personality is time-urgency: one must be doing things, achieving goals, competing against self or others, or accomplishing "missions". Being mindfully still and "doing nothing" is usually taken by types A's for loafing; therefore, a waste of time.

If you read the biographies of great men and women throughout history you will find a common thread (or sutra) that links their lives: when they seemed to have reached a dead-end in their endeavors, inspiration came to them while they were engaged in "doing nothing"... sometimes even in their sleep!

Go quietly to a particular outdoor spot where you feel good, sit comfortably and immerse yourself in doing things of no practical value whatsoever, like watching the clouds in the sky or ants walking single file. Witness a sunrise or a sunset, scan objects in the horizon...or merely spend your time feeling the breeze over your skin, the song of a bird, or the smell of wet grass ... This is a valuable investment in your health that will sharpen your awareness and enhance your feelings of peace and harmony.

Indoors, you can achieve the same results by intensely observing a painting, a photograph, or a Yantra (a pure geometric configuration, composed of basic primal shapes that constitute psychological symbols corresponding to inner states of human consciousness). In fact, any visual object will do. Visual stimuli is a training aid we can use to focus our mind in a single point –the unmovable spot or Bindu in Yoga- thus avoiding becoming easy prey of our habitual obsessions.

Eating

Eating can also be a form of meditation if you take your time to breathe, chew and swallow the food properly and not rush through it while watching the 6:00 PM news. One trick is to put down your eating utensils and rest your hands on your lap while you chew.

Take your time to enjoy: look at your food carefully, then, close your eyes and discover nuances in the fragrance, texture and taste of your meals! Re-discover the smell of the food; after all, you do smell the wine, right? The sense of smell is the most important sense while eating! We all know how flavorless the food feels when having a cold, it's like eating cardboard. ☹.

Edgar Cayce

In my humble opinion Mr. Cayce was an American mystic. Daily, for over 40 years, Mr. Cayce would lay down on a couch, close his eyes; fold his hands in his lap and put himself in trance-like sort of state. While in this deep meditative state he was able to connect himself with "all time and space"; in this self-induced "sleep" he was able to provide insights on topics such as the mystery of reincarnation, cures for life-threatening illnesses, even the whereabouts of missing persons. Not only is Mr. Cayce famous for his psychic abilities, but also because he was many years ahead of his time. He was one of the first to talk about holistic health, a concept which states that our well-being depends on the totality of ourselves. The mind, physical, emotions, breathing, good posture and diet all blend into one physical, mental and spiritual being. He has been called "the father of holistic medicine."

In the 1930's a group of his associates asked Mr. Cayce how they could develop the same spiritual gifts that he possessed. Under his tutelage, they met every week for about 10 years to hold discussions on many topics; at the end of this time they had all become spiritually gifted. The themes they discussed on their weekly meetings were registered in two books: A Search for God Part I and Part II. Together with its related Study Guide, they are a perfect agenda for meditation practice. I used them with a group of friends for two years and I found them to be some of the most inspiring, deep, and organized material there is on meditation.

Edgar Cayce was born on March 18, 1877 in Hopkinsville, Kentucky and died on January 3, 1945 in Virginia Beach, Virginia, where the headquarters of the institution he helped found are located: The Association for Research & Enlightenment (see Appendix D).

Exercise
Good exercise is a mood-enhancer because it releases beta-endorphins, one of several morphine-like substances manufactured by the body to reduce stress and relieve pain. Endorphins are believed to produce four key effects on the body-mind: enhance the immune system, relieve pain, reduce stress, and postpone the aging process. Even though I do not recommend exercising to the point of exhaustion (any strength taken to an extreme becomes a weakness), it is my personal experience that when I work out at a high intensity I enter a trance-like state, and the monkeys of my mind stop their constant chattering. In moments such as these, the only thing that seems to matter is taking the next step or finishing the next repetition; afterwards, a great feeling of peace or quietude overwhelms me.

Hobbies
Jnana Yoga is the yoga of knowledge, the path to enlightenment through knowledge. Hobbies are what I call *fun knowledge*, something we don't have to do, but do it anyway because we feel good about it. Hobbies help us develop concentration, mindfulness and intuitive creativity; all of which are present when we meditate. The key is to transfer the passion we feel for our hobbies to everything we do!

Hypnosis
Sometimes we need professional help to unravel behavioral patterns, fears or anxieties that are deeply ingrained in our subconscious mind. In this sense, my experience with hypnosis was very favorable.

I had a personal mystery I wanted to investigate and somebody suggested I try hypnosis. I wanted to know why, after I had my heart attack, I felt panic whenever I went to see a doctor or anyone, for that matter, that wanted to take my blood pressure. I went to see a state licensed hypnologist and this is what I discovered under a hypnotic trance...

As a child growing up in the 1940's, I used to get sick very often. At that time there were no pediatricians and doctors usually treated kids like miniature adults. My mother took me to an excellent physician, Dr. Font-Suarez; who was very austere looking. I recalled that every time I went there I got some injection or a very painful 1940's treatment. What I had totally obliterated from my mind was that at the doctor's waiting room there was a big black and white painting depicting a doctor pulling a naked woman wrapped in sheets by the right arm. Her **left arm** was held and pulled by the bony fingers of Death, who was wearing a black cape and a terrifying skeletal grin.

Waiting for my turn in that office I used to sit for hours in front of this picture that represented the deadly tug-of-war between medicine, humanity and death. One day the stress of it was so much that I couldn't bear it any longer, I ran out of the doctor's office and dashed down the street. My mother desperately ran after me but I was too fast for her, hence she shouted for somebody to please stop me... a man grabbed me by my **left arm** and stopped my flight. As a small 7 year-old child I had reached the following conclusion:

Doctor's Offices = Pain = Death = Get the heck out of the doctor's office!

As I mentioned before, I had succeeded in removing the painting and the accompanying incident from my conscious mind... however, to my subconscious mind it was fresh as yesterday! When I had the heart attack and my brush with death all of this was subconsciously reaffirmed; consequently, whenever I went to a doctor's office and someone grabbed me by the **left arm** to take my blood pressure I wanted to run but I could not! As a result of this repressed urge to flee my blood pressure rose! The moral is: there are mysteries in our lives that are best solved by the skillful means of wellness professionals, and we should be thankful that we have these services available to us!

One more thing: when you are hypnotized by a professional hypnologist, you remember everything that happens in the session and you are fully in control at all times, consequently there is nothing to be afraid of. Of course, make sure you hire the services of a state licensed medical professional.

Mall, The
Type A's in general don't like long shopping sprees, it strains their patience; this stress factor increases exponentially if the Type A in question is a man.

Generally speaking, men at the mall focus on one thing only: the items they are going to buy. This is the result of millions years of evolution, during which men developed the hunter's mentality, which makes them focus on one thing: the *prey*. To the hunter, nothing else matters but the *prey*. On the other hand, women in general have the gatherer's mentality; they are more opportunistic than men and have superbly trained their peripheral vision, which I think is why they tend to know where everything is in the house. When at the mall, they're as comfortable as a fish in water. They will pick up a shiny little object with the corner of the eye, a mile away! Of course, there are exceptions to these generalizations!

When I go to the mall with my wife, I usually accompany her for a while, then I sit and, as a good Type A, I 'keep guard' over the stuff we already have while she continues shopping. This is the meditation I do while sitting at the mall: I try to watch people without judging, labeling or criticizing them... and I watch my mind (or rather, my monkeys) jump around. Sounds simple, but I dare you to try it! It's a lot of fun to watch the monkeys of the mind jumping from judgment to judgment! This challenge will have you looking forward to your next trip to the mall.

Laughter and/or Crying

Paradoxical as it might seem, these opposites of human emotions have one thing in common: when properly handled they can be great anti-stress options and gateways to meditation.

-Healing Through Laughter – If you search the Internet under two criteria, health and laughter, you will get over 386,000 hits. You will see web pages on the therapeutic healing of laughter for any ailment from cancer to arthritis, pages on healing through humor and laughter.

I have no doubts when I say that in America we hold the patent on humor. I am sure that there are more stand-up comedians and sit-coms per capita in the USA than any other place in the world. We laugh about ourselves and about our leaders, our irreverence knows no limits. We all agree that laughter makes us feel good and that it can heal us.

Looking at my own life in retrospective I realized that, previous to suffering the heart attack in 1984 I had lost my sense of humor. I started to worry too much and became intensely serious. I have observed that this is a major indicator which, combined with other stressors, can have terrible consequences on your health. Keep present that there is always time to laugh (especially about ourselves), that there is always time to watch a comedy and to share a joke. Some of the healthier (and happier) people I have met on the face of this planet always have the time to tell a joke or listen to one.

Look at yourself in my mirror; the minute you notice you are starting to behave too seriously go and watch a comedy and don't be afraid to laugh to your heart's content. If you are under medical treatment, I certainly do not recommend you abandon your treatment, just add laughter to help boost your immune system!

-Healing Through Crying – If you are a man then you probably don't know about women's best kept secret: crying is a number one de-stressor. Type A personalities usually don't cry, because they have more important things to do than to cry, and, if they would, they wouldn't be Type A's; so it's an oxymoron. Ha!

In my feeble attempts to understand the mysteries of this universe, right after my heart attack I met a very brilliant and unconventional teacher called Bhagwan Shree Rajneesh, who later changed his name to Osho (See Appendix C). At that time I was in a phase between bargaining and depression, as proposed by Dr. Elizabeth Kübler-Ross, the recently deceased psychiatrist who did pioneer work on death and dying. She described that we go through five stages whenever we are diagnosed with a catastrophic illness: denial, anger, bargaining, depression and acceptance.

When I met Osho I was willing to try anything that could lift me up from this dreadful condition. One of the techniques that he used was a laughing and crying meditation. It was very simple: under the supervision of a teacher we were instructed to laugh as much as we could, and so we did. Initially our laughter felt fake, but, as we laughed, we eventually let go of our inhibitions; then we laughed about ourselves and about others to our heart's content. When we reached a crescendo the teacher instructed us, in a gentle way, to start crying...

I don't have the words to describe here what goes on when a group of grownups start bawling like babies; we were crying our hearts' out! The relief we felt at the end of the therapy was indescribable. My life changed for the better after this session, mostly because I broke the taboo about being a man and crying in public. By really letting go, I discovered that abandoning myself to sorrow was a uniquely cathartic experience. Once in a while, when I feel sad or depressed, instead of holding on to these emotions I let go and cry. I do it while I am alone because, even though I could do it in public, it would probably make others feel sad, or uncomfortable. For their sake I prefer to do it privately. It is amazing how quickly guilt, depression, fear, anger or any other heavy emotion can be released by crying instead of holding on to it; the phrase 'let it out of your chest' is quite adequate to describe the sense of relief we feel afterwards.

Movies

Hollywood has all the answers – if you know where to look! I suggest you get together with a group of friends to watch a movie each month at someone's house or have everybody watch the movie separately and then meet to discuss it. You will be amazed by how much you can accelerate your learning process by sharing your mental resources with a group of friends. Here are some suggestions for the meetings:

-Every time the group meets take a couple of deep breaths hold hands and state the purpose of your meeting (i.e. Self Improvement). This will help set the mood.

-Set a fixed amount of time for the discussion of the movie, this will prevent the meeting from dragging on forever.

-Assign a moderator that will allow everyone to give their impressions of the film, maybe by asking questions on how the film applies to your life. Avoid being aloof, share your energy with others without monopolizing the conversation, and everyone will have a chance to express themselves.

-Since we have the tendency to compete, be aware that if you all agree to share something more than water when visiting each other, this can balloon into wine, cheese and eventually 3 course dinners! This is fine, though, if everybody agrees on it. Rotate hosts each month.

-Finish the meeting by holding hands in a circle and giving thanks.

Following is over one year's worth of very interesting films. It doesn't matter if you have seen them already, see them again under the light of self-improvement, and you will be surprised by how much 'juice' is still left in them.

> Dead Poet's Society – Robin Williams
> The Doctor – William Hurt
> Grand Canyon – Danny Glover, Kevin Kline

Ground Hog Day – Bill Murray
Gulliver's Travels (1996-TV) – Ted Danson
Little Buddha – Keanu Reeves
Radio – Cuba Gooding Jr.
Shall We Dance – Richard Gere – Jennifer Lopez
Sliding Doors – Gwyneth Paltrow
Seven Years in Tibet – Brad Pitt
Super Size Me – Morgan Spurlock.
Under the Tuscan Sun – Diane Lane
What Dreams May Come – Robin Williams
What the "*Bleep*" Do We Know?

You can have the same type of meeting to discuss books. Think of this event as group, or *collective*, meditation! ☺

Pets – Our gift from nature!

A study published in 1995 in the American Journal of Cardiology concludes that people with pets have better survival rates over catastrophic illnesses than those that don't have pets.

The National Institutes of Health have conducted studies that show that persons that have pets tend to have lower triglycerides, cholesterol and blood pressure levels. Pets are currently used in some hospitals just for the gratification and well-being they offer to the patients in exchange for a few strokes. Other studies show that pets bring laughter, relaxation and companionship into our lives; in general, pets appeal to our better self.

I live in the countryside bordering a rain forest reserve, the perfect place for my two dogs, a Labrador Retriever, and a cross between Dalmatian and Labrador. As a kid I never had any pets because we lived in the city in a small house and my mother made perfectly clear that she had her hands full with four children. I repeated the same mantra while raising mine. Now that the nest is empty, here I am, 63 years old and enjoying these two dogs, my first pets.

In my short time (4 years) as a pet owner I have come to appreciate their eagerness to please me... They act as if they had no regrets or sorrows; they hold no grudges against me whatsoever and seem to live intensely in the present moment. I have yet to meet someone, family members included, who looks so overjoyed by my arrival!

I don't pretend to be an expert on the effects of pet-owning and health, but based on my recent experiences, I believe they make me a happier person and this may well have added quality years to my life... and by improving my health they have also improved the quality of my meditation.

Praying

Every one has a unique way of praying and that is fine. Praying will induce a state of deep concentration that leads to a meditative state and a quiet mind. I will mention here a few unique praying styles that have caused a favorable impression in me and that might be of interest to you.

-**Reciting the alphabet** – I once met a Tibetan child that told me that every morning, when she wakes up, she recites the alphabet and then decrees the following: "May all the words that I utter today using these letters bring love and joy to all who hear them."

-**Using a Bell** – A couple friends of mine (Ivan & Ivette Figueroa) gave me as a present a big Chinese bell I keep next to the entrance. This is how I sometimes pray these days: I have realized (finally!) that I am an ignorant and that I really don't know the consequences of what to ask for. I ring the bell and ask God, the Divinity or the Transcendental Wisdom to please pick up the sounds that are necessary to bring love and compassion into this troubled world... sort of *praying by proxy*.

-**Prayer Flags** – Also a Tibetan tradition – Write your favorite prayer, best wish, positive thought or mantra on a piece of cloth and tie it outside your house on a pole or tree, or let it hang out a window seeing that when the wind blows it will move and spread these blessings out into the world like a sweet fragrance.

Reading

I was born in 1942; during my childhood there was no TV, therefore I was raised on books and radio. Books expanded my mind beyond all horizons, by age fourteen I had voraciously read all the novels, comic books and articles that had fallen into my hands.

To give you a better idea, by the time I was fourteen I had read Don Quixote, ten out of the twenty-four Tarzan novels, the full collection of Edgar Allan Poe's novels and poems, all the novels by Jules Verne, quite a bit of Shakespeare and many, many other renowned authors. I must thank my mother for encouraging me to develop this habit. Books are still my friends... through them I have found recreation, wisdom, solace, and strength in moments of great need in my life. Needless to say, I have read several times from cover to cover, one of the all-time best-sellers... The Bible. Great religious texts like The Bible, The Koran, The Mahabharata or The Dhammapada, have always been great sources of inspiration and meditation for faithful practitioners. Honor your spiritual heritage and use them!

Included here are excerpts from seven additional contemporary books that have helped me enormously in reaching a state of equanimity and balance in my life. It is my wish that they might do the same for you.

-How to Eat, Move and Be Healthy!- By Paul Chek "Your personalized 4-step guide to looking and feeling great from the inside out." This visually attractive and easy to read book presents revolutionary concepts that are the result of thorough scientific research by Mr. Chek and his Institute. Topics such as: "If Einstein was your doctor", "The no-diet diet", "You are what and when you eat", "Determining your metabolic type", "Are you getting on bed on time?" and other important topics enable you to custom-tailor a holistic program that will greatly improve the quality of your life.

-The Celestine Prophecy by James Redfield, a sociologist that worked for over 15 years with abused children, makes us aware through his book of the fact that, even though we live in a world made up of energy, almost everybody feels that there is not enough of it to go around. Because of this "mentality of scarcity" we use different behavioral strategies to "acquire" energy from each other. Redfield defines these as: The Intimidator, The Poor Me, The Interrogator, and The Aloof.

The **Intimidator** Strategy – Violence is his middle name– "You do what I say or else…."

The **Poor Me** Strategy – "Nobody understands my suffering." This becomes a valid strategy to deal with an Intimidator – "I am dying here, can't you see?". It usually disarms the Intimidator.

The **Interrogator** Strategy – "What, When, How, Why? - Tell me!" Parents commonly use this strategy with their children, trying to control them by denying their approval.

The **Aloof** Strategy– "Talk to the Hand" or "Wallpaper Flower" is the strategy that protects our energy from an Interrogator that is trying to suck us dry with his/her questioning.

The Celestine Prophecy gave me great insights on how to set up meetings in an energy efficient way to obtain the maximum results for all the different types of participants involved.   The book also contains a lot of insights on how to make the right choices when you look at things from a "meditative" perspective.

-The Teachings of Samael Aun Weor – To me, The *Gnostics* (see Appendix D) are the "Special Forces of Meditation"; what I mean by this is that they are really intense practitioners who won't compromise their belief on the great harm humanity is causing to the planet, each other, and to all sentient beings that share it with us. They believe we generate this harmful activity because of our deeply ingrained egos.

The Gnostics also use the energetic model of the universe. Their meditation techniques are aimed to identify and recycle the energy permeating the universe. They believe that, instead of having all of
80

our energy available to us in a big vat , our energy is fragmented and bottled up in tiny flasks which don't allow us the proper use of all our resources.   These tiny flasks bear the labels of fear, envy, resentment, hate, criticism, jealousy, anger, attachment, etc., that we keep for our father, mother, husband, wife, brother, sister, neighbor, boss, and of course politicians and so on and so forth…

If you feel you need to go to a "meditation boot camp" then the Gnostics are for you because they don't beat around the bush, let me tell you that. This path requires great effort but the reward is huge… at the end you will have all your available energy in one big container labeled: "Love and Compassion for all".

-The Orange Book: The Meditation Techniques of Bhagwan Shree Rajneesh (Osho) Osho was one of the great meditation teachers of the 20th century, his book is a must for the serious meditator.   It has all kinds of superb and unique meditation techniques; refer to Appendix C for his web site. I can't recommend it enough!

-Heal Your Body A-Z by Louise L. Hay Louise L. Hay has a remarkable story of self-healing. Her childhood was unstable and impoverished, and her teen years were marked by abuse. As an adult she developed cancer. She underwent several surgeries until one day she decided it was enough.   She postponed her upcoming surgery and started to work with her teacher to clear old patterns of resentment using the antidote of forgiveness; simultaneously she made significant changes in her nutrition and completely detoxified her body. In her own words: "So between the mental and physical cleansing, in six months I was able to get the medical Profession to agree with what I already knew: I no longer had any form of cancer."

Based on her remarkable experience, she wrote this amazing book that tells us how to substitute the old mental patterns that can possibly make us ill with new and positive affirmations. Here, the mental causes for physical illness are linked to negative thought patterns and beliefs that need to be overcome; moreover, the book is easy to read and very well-indexed (problem – probable cause - new healthier mental pattern). Her superb work helped me enormously to recuperate from my heart attack, it can probably help you,   Also see Sound-Mantras page 86.

-Methods of Traditional Chinese Health Care- by Zen Qinqnam. Don't judge a book by its cover, much less by its size! This little booklet is packed with an amazing arsenal of effective yet deceivingly simple self-healing techniques based on the ancient Chinese practices of acupuncture, herbal medicine and Qi-gong. Remember: it doesn't have to look like a pill or a surgeon's knife to cure us!

Like Yoga, Pilates, or any other type of exercise, this booklet is great for active meditation; it also complements the practice of those who enjoy sitting and "doing nothing". This booklet empowers you to help yourself, to assist you in vanquishing that sense of helplessness western medicine creates in patients by the mere fact that *patients are expected to play a passive role in their treatment and recovery.*

-Light on Yoga- by B.K.S. Iyengar I have mentioned several times throughout this booklet that Yoga is a complete discipline for improving your body and mind. It is so accessible that you don't even need shoes to practice Yoga, maybe just a mat. Yoga is one of India's gift to humanity. Its beginnings have been traced to two important ancient cities: Mohenjo-Daro and Harappa, in the Indus Valley, a region centered between what is today the border between Pakistan and India, but that could have extended all the way to Bombay in the east and Afghanistan in the west. It is speculated that the origins of Yoga might go back to 8,000 B.C. and for certain 5,000 BC. Now think: what exercise program, or for that matter, what human endeavor has lasted for 5,000 years or possibly 8,000 years? Answer: *very, very few.*

The word Yoga comes from *Sanskrit*, India's ancient and now dead language, and it means to yoke, to bring together. It gently guides us into finding the union between a runaway mind and a stranded body, by making us conscious of how we eat, breathe, think, move, meditate, and pray. Once we achieve this, it is easier to become aware of the connection, the *thread* (sutra) that unites us all. There are 8 steps in Yoga that we must master to reach this state of harmony ...

1st – Be good to others or *Yamas*
2nd –Be good to yourself or *Niyamas*
3rd – Exercise consciously or *Asanas*
4th – Practice the art/science of breathing or P*ranayamas*
5th – Separate your mind from the senses or P*ratyahara*
6th – Master the art of concentration or D*harana*
7th - Master the art of meditation or D*hyana*
8th – Reach total harmony or *Samadhi.*

After 20 years of practicing and teaching Yoga, I have understood beyond intellectual learning, **I know**, that everything in this universe is interrelated, interdependent, and even though appearances might lead us to think that we are separate from the rest of creation, this is not true. A mother that loses a child in Siberia, a man that gets a well-deserved promotion in Patagonia affect us all because events disseminate throughout the universe like concentrical waves rippling in a pond when a pebble falls into it. The universe is the "pond" and the pebble is the "event"; since we are all in the same pond, sooner or later all events will affect us, the degree to which we will be affected depends on the event's magnitude and how close we are to it.

Now, going back to Mr. Iyengar… his encyclopedic work on Yoga has 590 photographs, 200 postures and a very reasonable price. The inspiration you will derive just from the Foreword by violinist Yehudi Menuhin, the Preface and the Introduction are priceless. You will also find thorough explanations on how to execute different Yoga poses giving due considerations to your level of skill, hence you will benefit from the postures, regardless   you are a beginner, intermediate or advanced practitioner.   As if this was not enough, in Appendix II of his book, Yogacharia B.K.S. Iyengar details the adequate yoga postures (asanas) to relieve many illnesses that afflict the human body and mind. I highly recommend this book as a treasure of bodily and mental health.

Sleep (Dream Yoga)

Most people don't know that it is possible to meditate while asleep! Once you acquire a certain degree of mindfulness during your daily activities you will be able to extend your meditation practice to your sleeping hours. Before I go on I would like to mention that messing around with your sleeping time could have terrible consequences for your health, be extra careful with these techniques.

Here is a fairly simple one: every once in a while during the day pull on your index fingers with the opposite hand and ask yourself: I am dreaming or awake? Eventually you will see your hands in one of your dreams and you will pull on your finger while dreaming... your index finger is going to stretch like it was made of rubber, wow! When this happens you will realize you are dreaming; while in this state of awareness you will be able to voluntarily affect your dream, change it or hold it steady. This is called *lucid dreaming*; it is a dream state where you know you are dreaming and can willingly change or affect the contents of your dream. It requires a lot of concentration, energy and effort; and it can usually be achieved once we have reclaimed some of the scattered energy we have invested in our egos.

The Gnostics are experts on these techniques. You will also read about this type of experience in Carlos Castaneda's novels, where he expounds extensively on "the dream world", a mysterious and esoteric world that requires a special personal disposition. If this interests you, I recommend you look for a teacher. By the way, an interesting fact is that tobacco (nicotine) helps induce lucid dreams; maybe this is why Native Americans used it in their ceremonies.

Silva Mind Control – In late 1984 I went to a seminar promoted by an institution called Silva Mind Control where I met Rosa Ellen Rodríguez (RIP), a psychologist and the instructor for the seminar. At that time the course covered things that nowadays are common knowledge, but back then were revolutionary, at least on this part of the world. It introduced us to things like the benefits of meditation, ESP, breathing, biofeedback, using dreams to help us solve our problems, and many other interesting and helpful techniques. Mr. Silva had realized that good things happen to us when we lower our brain waves to around 8 cycles per second or *the alpha wave range*. He devised many ways of teaching people how to achieve that state, and the course taught us exactly that.

Being an electrical engineer, I liked the fact that the course was scientifically oriented and that there was no religion or spirituality involved in it. For a few years I explored his method, went to seminars held by Mr. Silva himself and was positively inspired by him and Rosa Ellen. Many of the techniques I learned in their seminars I later realized were ratified by other disciplines. Please refer to Appendix C for their web page address.

Sound – Listening

The quality of the sounds we hear effects our emotions in much the same way as the quality of the food we eat affects our body. The vibrations that we hear have repercussions according to their nature; they can soothe, disturb, or have a neutral effect on our mind. Words, being sounds, have an effect that can be amplified tenfold, even a hundredfold, depending on their message and on how our mind interprets them.

Listening to sounds without judging is a skillful art that requires constant training; the moment we judge or label a sound, the *act* of listening shape-shifts into a *mental concept*. This becomes either a restriction to openness; or it can generate an emotion leading to attachment or aversion. It's quite a challenge to sit quietly and listen to sounds without judging, maintaining an attitude of equanimity. Our thoughts have a way of becoming "solid" when we label and judge our perceptions, thoughts and sensations. As a result, emotions arise from this mental process which, in turn, engage and exert demands from the endocrine system as if we were experiencing a real thing, and not a mental construct. It is easy to imagine hormones rushing through our body, causing it to physically respond with a fight or flight reaction in response to alarming, threatening thoughts.

As an exercise, try this: sit quietly, take a couple of deep abdominal breaths (page 55) and concentrate on the sounds you hear without judging them or elaborating on them. If you find yourself judging, mentally say to yourself: *judging*, and go back to listening. If the sounds are upsetting, I find the following mantra very useful: *"Nothing disturbs my peace"*.

Sound-Mantras

According to The Encyclopedia of Eastern Philosophy and Religion, "Mantra is a word in Sanskrit, India's ancient language that through

its repetition can protect our mind from itself!" It is my experience that mantras protect us from our own negative mental obsessions. A mantra doesn't have to be in Sanskrit; you will agree with me that we are constantly using mantras in our own language. For instance, "I can do it!" is an example of a positive mantra, while "I feel miserable" is an example of a negative mantra.

Don't underestimate the power of words. When we verbally utter a positive thought, the words that come out of our mouth reenter our brain through our ears, thus reinforcing our positive mental patterns. Of course, the same thing will happen with negative affirmations. Remember the Law of Facilitation in Neurology: "When an impulse passes once through a given set of neurons to the exclusion of others, it will tend to do so on a future occasion; and each time it traverses this path the resistance will be smaller." A mantra will facilitate neural pathways in our brain until they make the way we think about something automatic or habitual.

Thus, mantras are not only words that we mentally or verbally repeat to ourselves, or the words we hear others say about themselves or about us... but, think about it... the lyrics of a song could also be a mantra, especially if it happens to be a popular song, played in the media over and over! Don't underestimate the power of words, *be very careful of what you let get through to your heart.*

Sound – Music

There are certain musical sounds that promote harmony in our mind and body. Mozart's music is known for producing a calming, soothing effect. Gregorian chanting, a bell ringing inside its dome in a church, the sound of running water, and many others have similar effects. Nevertheless, musical taste is very personal; I suggest you experiment with musical sounds, instruments and composers until you find the right combination that calms and soothes you. Once you find what works, you may use it in meditation, or during your daily activities, to restore tranquility and quiet the mind.

Tai Chi (Pronounced Tahe- Chee)
Its roots go back to China thousands of years. This ancient martial art-science, like Yoga, promotes mindful movement as a way of leading a healthy life that is physically and mentally balanced. T'ai Chi proposes that we are immersed in an ocean of energy (Chi) that we can harvest and use to release energy blockages or even nourish insufficiencies in our bodies. This is achieved by executing specific slow movement patterns and by pressing or needling certain points in our body. In Appendix D you will find a couple of books and Web Sites that have helped me understand and use this abundant good energy that surrounds us.

I suspect the energy we call "Chi" is some form of electromagnetic energy. Our heart, besides being a blood pump is also an *electromagnetic generator*. Certain studies indicate the possibility of electromagnetic communication between the heart and the brain, not only in any given person, but also between the hearts and brains of different persons! (Rollin McCraty, PhD, William A. Tiller, PhD and Mike Atkinson. In: *Proceedings of the Brain-Mind Applied Neuro-physiology EEG*, Neurofeedback Meeting, Key West, Florida, 1996.) One more reason to develop a compassionate attitude and loving kindness in our hearts!

Tarot
The history of the tarot cards can be traced back to northern Italy in the 1600's from there it evolved to the present deck configuration of 78 cards divided in four suits: wands representing the element *fire*, cups representing the element *water*, pentacles representing the element *earth*, and spades representing the element *air*. Each suit has numbered cards 1-10 and four court cards for a total of 14 cards.

These constitute a total of 56 *minor arcana* cards, to which we must add the 22 *major arcana* cards (numbered 0-21), for a grand total of 78 cards. The *major arcana* contain pictorial representations of various cosmic forces such as *Death, Justice, Strength,* and so on; while the remainder *minor arcana* represent specific opportunities and lessons, people, relationships, finances, action, energies, and other forces.

The Tarot taps into the unconscious mind since it is very visual and rich in *archetypes* (potent universal symbols appearing in myths, fairytales and dreams) that appeal to the *subconscious* level of the mind; I have no doubts that working with the cards will help you unravel some of the mysteries in your life.

The images from the Tarot deck can be related to the analytical psychology of Carl Gustav Jung. The famous Swiss psychiatrist (1876-1961), founder of analytic psychology, had a prolific and productive life. He graduated in medicine in 1902 from the University of Basel in Zurich, he also had a wide background in biology, zoology, paleontology, and archaeology. Part of his observations, hypothesis and theories were based on extensive field work he personally conducted among aboriginal tribes in several continents. He coined several terms that influenced the way we think, some of which are: *Archetypes, Collective Subconscious*, and *Synchronicity*. These three concepts are key for the understanding of the Tarot deck.

Archetypes are mental images that have the same universal meaning regardless of the culture where they appear. Jung postulated that they are passed from parents to siblings as part of our common human heritage. For example: an image that represents moving up means to ascend, to triumph. On the other hand images that depict moving down mean defeat, to be unsuccessful; to mankind these are universal concepts.

Collective Subconscious is part of *our subconscious mind*. To Jung our subconscious mind has two aspects: the first aspect is *our own individual subconscious* which contains our personal experiences; it might be too weak to come forward into the conscious mind or it might have been purposefully suppressed by the conscious mind if deemed too threatening. The second aspect is a *universal or collective subconscious mind* that we all share by the mere fact of being human. The archetypes are part of this universal subconscious.

Synchronicity – This refers to the interaction of phenomena that seems to spring isolated in one person but synchronizes and manifests in the physical world of another person with no previous sequential causes or effects ("a causal"). Refer to the introductory chapter (Learning Through Suffering) as an example of how I experienced this phenomena in my own flesh and blood.

It is believed that the tarot somehow "connects", for lack of a better word, with these three principles, bringing about some remarkable results in our lives through its use. It's like having our own private therapist!

I was introduced to the ancient art of the tarot through the Robin Wood Tarot deck, which comes with an instruction manual. I find this deck to be perfect for beginners because its images are vivid and easy to understand; its symbols are not obscure and the images are not abstract, which makes them very easy to interpret.

I also have a rule that has made it a lot simpler for me to use the tarot. I don't deal upside down cards because I have a hard time figuring out exactly how I should interpret them; they might mean the opposite of their right side up, or a blockage on the energy represented by the card, or a diminution of the energy depicted! So, I keep my cards always upright in my deck. I figured there are enough upright cards in the deck meaning the opposite of each other; if "needed", the right one will show up in a reading.

The instruction book will guide you on how to deal certain configurations like a cross, a square, etc., but the truth of the matter is that you can use any single card to meditate. That is, every day you can pull just one card from the deck and meditate on its positive and negative attributes and on how they apply to you, your life situations the decisions you have to make in your life. Please remember, the main thing is to have fun with the tarot...don't take it too seriously! You can <u>always</u> look at the positive aspect of the cards. Have Fun!

"The Question"

There is nothing new under the sun, but I like to think this is an original idea (sorry, there are still some egos in me!). It goes like this: when meditating, formulate a question about something that intrigues you. It could be about a very down-to-earth topic like, "Why is the ocean blue?" or about something deeper, like: "I want irrefutable evidence on reincarnation, does it or doesn't it exist?" You won't have to wait too long, usually the answer will be revealed from where you least expect it...maybe your barber will drop the answer casually, or the kid next door will make a comment too wise for his age.

The challenge is to be wide awake, as if you were stalking a prey, if not, you could miss the answer. Whenever we ask profound questions it's always good to add an important clause...*we don't want the answer to come to us wrapped in pain and suffering, there's enough suffering in the world as it is*! I believe we deserve to learn our lessons gently and in a joyful manner. The answer must be delivered with love and compassion. As I already mentioned, in the beginning you will be surprised when the answers start popping at you from where you least expect them, but after a while you will take this for granted. Have fun! ☺

Therapeutic Massage

Since I work as a Holistic Exercise Instructor at the Golden Door Spa at El Conquistador Resort in Puerto Rico, the therapeutic value of touch does not escape me. There therapists here have a saying: "We carry our issues in our tissues." This makes massage an invaluable tool in well-being and healing. One therapeutic massage can have an effect equivalent to a dozen meditation sessions. The soothing effect a massage has in your nervous, lymphatic, muscular, skeletal and endocrine system is indescribable; you have to try it to feel the enormous benefit it can produce in your body, mind and soul. **Therapeutic massages are a must for type A's.** **I can't emphasize it enough.**

However there are some <u>major</u> misconceptions about therapeutic massages, namely: that they have little health benefits to offer or that they are <u>very</u> expensive and are only meant for women who have nothing else to do than go to a spa. Some people even erroneously think that there's an erotic (sexual) component to all forms of massage. That is why I named this section _therapeutic massage_. This type of massage is administered by a <u>professional therapist</u> which has gone through in-depth training covering anatomy, physiology, over a dozen therapeutic treatment modalities, and last, but not least, has passed a state certification exam and has a license to prove it.

A good therapist will be able to tell you what type of massage (Shiatsu, Swedish, Thai, La Stone, Cranio-Sacral, etc.) depending on your overall health condition will benefit you the most and, after the session, will also be able to give you feedback about balance and tension in your body. This information is very important because it provides clues about postural and muscular imbalances you can use to start re-creating harmony in your life. Muscles reflect not only the state of the physical body but also our mindset; remember, everything is interrelated.

Price range will vary depending on many conditions, but in my experience working at a superb spa like The Golden Door, the average cost of a therapeutic massage may go from a little over a hundred dollars for a 50 minute treatment up to around two hundred dollars for an 80 minute session. And believe me, they're worth every penny... you'll feel so good and so energized afterward! Consider it a reasonable investment in your health...why? Let me give you an example... On November 1997 I was visiting relatives in Orlando, Florida. One day, after eating very spicy dinner I became constipated and the lower left part of my abdomen became very tender. I though it was just indigestion but, after living with discomfort, bloating and pain for a couple of days I decided to go to the Columbia Park Hospital Emergency Room.

Once there they took my blood pressure, did routine blood tests and an x-ray of my abdomen. These all took about an hour, after which they made me wait an additional four hours. Finally, a doctor showed up for five minutes and told me I had diverticulitis, wrote a prescription for antibiotics and released me from the hospital. I was billed $1,804.25. This was 1997, I am sure that by now these costs have increased considerably. If this was the cost for a non-life-threatening condition, how much do you think it costs to spend one day in coronary intensive unit? For sure over $5,000 per day. Now with this money, how many massages could you afford if they helped you improve your health and saved you a trip to the hospital? If you were to save yourself <u>one day at the hospital</u>, this would amount to about 50 massages; or enough for one massage a week for a year! With this kind of therapy you can say good-by to sore muscles and stressful mental patterns. I can guarantee it will be more enjoyable than one expensive day in the hospital. Take my word, I've been there, done that.

Visualizations

-Color Breathing – Sit comfortably, take a few deep breaths with long exhalations and choose a color, any color, as long as it is bright. Imagine that when you inhale you inhale this bright color and when you exhale you exhale it through your heart. If any part of your body is sore or in pain, imagine that you exhale this color through it, and that the color soothes and heals this part of your body.

-White Stream or Light – Close your eyes and imagine your own image sitting in front of yourself. From the center of your heart a stream of pure, white light goes to the heart of your image. This white light represents love, compassion, joy, health, patience, and all the good qualities that make us feel happier. Keep sending the stream of white, pure light until your image shines intensely, radiating light in all directions. You can also use this visualization exercise with your loved ones, your friends, and even those who are not quite your friends.

Writing – Meditative writing by Dr. Ira Progoff

A few years ago I took Dr. Progoff's Intensive Journal Writing Workshop. This program taught me how to use writing as a meditation tool. This book is a result of that workshop. If you are inclined to put your thoughts in writing, Dr. Progoff's seminar is for you. Dr. Progoff, like Carl Jung (p.88), believed we share a common heritage, the *collective subconscious*, and that we can tap it for our own and mankind's benefit.

In Dr. Progoff's own words: "When our attention is focused inwardly at the depth of our inner being, in the context of the wholeness of our life, resources of a profound knowledge of life become accessible to us." "The Intensive Journal process is our inner workshop, the place where we do the creative shaping of the artwork of our life."

Dr. Progoff's Journal is a highly organized, meditative path into these resources, but, like everything else, developing writing skills requires practice.

ZEN

According to The Encyclopedia of Eastern Philosophy and Religion, "Zen is the Japanese abbreviation of the word *zenna*, the Japanese way of reading Chinese *channa*. This, in turn, is the Chinese version of the Sanskrit word *dhyana* which refers to the collectedness of mind or the meditative absorption in which all dualistic distinctions like I/you, subject/object, and true/false are eliminated." Zen stresses the prime importance of the enlightenment experience and the uselessness of ritual religious practices and intellectual analysis of doctrine for attainment of liberation.

To me, Zen is meditation with no frills, in its purest form. For one year I went every Sunday to a Zen Temple where a group met and meditated under to tutelage of a Zen monk. We sat on our knees perfectly erect and still for at least one hour. In the beginning it was tough, and I mean really tough; I felt all kind of itches and urges. Gnostics call these itches and urges *the body of desires*. Nevertheless, after a few sessions, everybody got used to it and one hour passed very fast, at the end of which we felt refreshed and full of energy. After the sitting meditation we also did a *walking meditation*. We walked single file focusing our attention on where the preceding person had stepped. When you focus and concentrate your mind in such an intense way you manage to stop your internal chattering, worries will vanish and a feeling of peacefulness will suffuse you. If you want to sit quietly and move into stillness... try Zen meditation, it holds the patent.

Conclusion:

Initially, we might think that the ultimate goal of the meditation tools and techniques presented here is to soothe and harmonize our minds and bodies, but that really is the secondary goal. As we advance in our practice we will notice that inevitably, spontaneously, like the bee to the nectar, we will be drawn to the *source of everything that is...* we will be drawn to remember we are already *one* with Love and Compassion. This is the truth our spiritual teachers have been telling us for thousands of years, the ultimate reality where our true essence lies.

Appendix B

Your Goal's : A Check List

"Omne Rarum Carum"
Everything coveted is expensive.
- Latin Proverb -

I encourage you to use the check list of goals on the opposite page to keep track of your accomplishments in the life-long endeavor to replace old mental patterns with new and healthier ones.

If possible, perform the items in the order they are listed; but feel free to accommodate to your personal needs!

Check List of Goals	Due Date
1. My first 8 glasses of water per day	_____
2. My first 8 hours' sleep	_____
3. Family Life Assessment	_____
4. Workplace Assessment	_____
5. Social Life Assessment	_____
6. My Meditation Space Set Up	_____
7. My First Breathing Routine	_____
8. My First Concentration Drill	_____
9. My First Visualization	_____
10. Medical Check Up	_____
11 Metabolic Typing Diet Assessment	_____
12. Personal Trainer Assessment	_____
13. Physiological Load Assessment	_____
14. My First Exercise Routine*	_____
15. My First Therapeutic Massage	_____

* Could be Aerobics, Weights, Walking, Yoga, Tai-Chi, etc.

Appendix C

Bibliography, References

& Web Sites

" No Man is An Island."
John Donne

Anatomy
Anatomy of Hatha Yoga
David Coulter
ISBN 0-9707006-0-1

Body Electric, The
Robert O. Becker, M.D.
ISBN 0-688-06971-1

Gray's Anatomy
H. Gray, Drawings by H.V. Carter
ISBN 0-7607-2273-0

Structure & Function of the Body
Thibodaux – Patton
ISBN 0-323-02242-1

Trail Guide to the Body
Andrew Biel
ISBN 0-9658534-1-1

Health/Exercise – Mind/Body
Accu- Yoga
Reed – Marco
ISBN 0-87040-489-X

Book of Massage and Aroma Therapy, The
Nitya Lacroix
ISBN 0-517-10256-0

Fitness Theory and Practice
Aerobic & Fitness Association of America
ISBN 0-9638168-4-5

Heal Your Body A-Z
Louise L. Hay
ISBN: 1-56170-792-9

Healing Path of Yoga
Nishala Joy Devi
ISBN 0-609-80502-9

How to Eat, Move and Be Healthy!
Paul Chek
ISBN 1-58387-006-7

Light on Pranayama
B.K.S. Iyengar
ISBN 0-8245-0686-3

Light on Yoga
B.K.S. Iyengar
ISBN 0-8052-1031-8

Methods of Traditional Chinese Health Care
Zeng Qingnan
ISBN 7-119-01209-6

Wisdom of Forgiveness, The
Dalai Lama and Victor Chan
(ISBN 1-57322-277-1)

Nutrition:
The Crazy Makers – ISBN 1-58542-104-9
Natural Alternatives to Vioxx, Celebrex & Other Anti-
Inflammatory Prescription Drugs - ISBN 0-7570-0278-1.
Both by Carol Simontacchi

Meditation
Celestine Prophecy, The
James Redfield
ISBN 0-446-67100-2

Dream Dictionary
Tony Crisp
ISBN 0-440-23707-6

Great Rebellion, The; Gnostic Psychology and the Path to Liberation
from the Ego
Samael Aun Weor
ISBN: Amazon.com

Healing Cards
Caroline Myss and Peter Occhiogrosso
ISBN 1-4019-0023-2

On Death and Dying
Elisabeth Kübler-Ross, M.D.
ISBN 0-684-83938-5

Orange Book, The: The meditation techniques of Bhagwan Shree
Rajneesh (Meditation Series)
Osho
ISBN: Amazon.com

Secret Language of Dreams, The
David Fontana
ISBN 0-8118-0728-2

Search for God
Edgar Cayce
ISBN 87604-000-8

References
Webster's New World Dictionary
Gualnick, Editor in Chief
ISBN 60B 0-529-05324-1

Encyclopedia of Eastern Philosophy and Religion, The
Shumaker Et Al
ISBN 0-87773-433-X

Web Sites

A.R.E. (Association for Research and Enlightenment)
http://www.edgarcayce.org/

C.H.E.K. Institute – Leaders in Exercise Education
http://www.chekinstitute.com/

Effortless Diaphragmatic Breathing
http://www.bfe.org/protocol/pro10eng.htm

Ira Progoff's Intensive Journal
http://www.intensivejournal.org/

Osho – The Science of the Inner Meditation
http://www.osho.com/

NIOSH
National Institute for Occupation Safety and Health
http://www.cdc.gov/niosh/homepage.html

Perspective View – Personal development with emphasis on communication.
http://www.PerspectiveView.com

The Relaxation Response Organization
http://www.relaxationresponse.org/

Silva Mind Control
http://www.silvaultramindsystem.com/

Appendix D

The Making of a Monkey

Aaron McGruder

An ego is the result of investing our personal energy in an illusion, a screeching monkey that doesn't allow us to see, hear, or speak the truth... and as a result we suffer and make others suffer, too.

According to the Gnostics, these mental creations are so ingrained into us that getting rid of them would feel like skinning ourselves alive! Egos are nothing more than illusions, they don't have enough power to turn a small light bulb on... still, they enslave us. I have realized this through meditation and introspection, for example, have you ever argued with someone and known you were wrong but couldn't admit it? That is what I mean; we can't tolerate the slightest criticism toward any of our monkeys, we think we have too much energy invested in them to allow them to disappear.

Why do we choose then the path of suffering instead of the path of liberation? Meditation will give you the answer if you are willing to look for it... What can you loose? Future suffering generated by your reckless monkeys! What do you have to gain? Harmony, peace, tranquility and a healthier life!

Emilio Robles

Preparing…

Applying the latex…

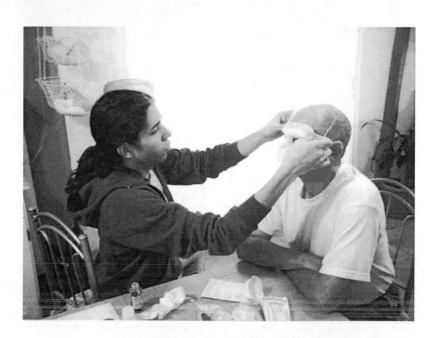

Fitting the prosthesis…

Getting there…

I can't believe it…

Ready to pose…

The monkey in me…

Happy ending: "The shedding off" the monkey…

About the Author

Emilio Robles is a Professional Electrical Engineer, Certified Data Processor, A+ and Network+ Certified, who worked with computers for over 30 years. In 1984 Mr. Robles was a typical type A person, highly driven, successful and... impatient. At age 42, in the pinnacle of his career, he suffered a heart attack that transformed his life physically, mentally and spiritually.

As a result he changed his bearings and moved from the city of San Juan to the mountains, close to a rain forest reserve where he rebuilt an old cabin of a house. He became certified in Yoga with the International Teachers Association (IYTA- based in Australia), also in Pilates, Precision Cycling, Resist-A-Ball, Aqua, and Group Exercise (AFAA). He is now a C.H.E.K. Institute Exercise Coach, and Nutritional Lifestyle Coach Level 1. He obtained a license from the Department of Education to teach Basic Anatomy and Physiology for the Institute of Massage and Therapeutic Healing in Fajardo, Puerto Rico. He also teaches Yoga and other holistic exercise disciplines at the Golden Door Spa at El Conquistador Hotel in Fajardo, Puerto Rico and lives happily in his rainforest house, with his Type B wife, also a certified holistic trainer, and two highly photogenic dogs.